THE
LIGHT-HEARTED COOKBOOK

RECIPES FOR A HEALTHY HEART

THE
LIGHT-HEARTED
COOKBOOK

ANNE LINDSAY

GRUB STREET · LONDON

Published by Grub Street, The Basement, 10 Chivalry Road, London SW11 1HT

This new edition copyright 1999
First UK impression 1991 (Reprinted 1991, 1993, 1994 and 1995)
Copyright © Heart and Stroke Foundation of Ontario, 1999
© Anne Lindsay & Associates Ltd., 1999
First published by Key Porter Books Limited, Toronto, Canada

British Library Cataloguing in Publication Data
Lindsay, Anne
    The light-hearted cookbook - New ed.
    1. Cookery 2. Heart - Diseases - Diet therapy - Recipes
    I.Title   II.British Heart Foundation
    641.5'6311

    ISBN 1902304152

Cover photograph by Simon Smith
Photographs by Fred Bird
Illustrations by Madeleine David
Design by Marie Bartholomew
Typesetting Chapterhouse
Printed and bound by Biddles Ltd, Guildford and King's Lynn

Contents

4. Appendices

ACKNOWLEDGEMENTS

My thanks to all those who made the original edition of this book possible especially Dr Anthony Graham, M.D., F.R.C.P. (C) for the many hours he volunteered. Thanks, to my best critics, my husband, Bob, and my teenage children, Jeff, John and Susie for their love and constant support.

Anne Lindsay

Grub Street wish to express their thanks to the British Heart Foundation for making this UK edition possible, especially Professor Desmond Julian, Consultant Medical Director and Heather Waring of the Education Department; and to Paula Hunt for all her nutritional expertise and hard work in editing this publication.

Preface

Anybody could be excused for being thoroughly confused by all the conflicting messages we receive on what we should and should not eat. As well as high profile battles between the manufacturers of butter and margarine, there are frequent skirmishes between proponents of a whole range of special diets and magic ingredients. Each debate tends to focus on one particular component of diet which is then elevated to the position of arch-villain in the cause of coronary heart disease or alternatively as a talisman, guaranteed to protect the individual. There is no single risk factor for coronary heart disease neither is there a guaranteed magic bullet food stuff or food supplement that will prevent it. We do however have a marvellous opportunity to reduce the risks both for ourselves and our families by eating a sensible and at the same time wholly enjoyable diet. The rules are simple. Eat plenty of fresh fruit and vegetables, cut down on fat intake, particularly saturated fats of animal origin, and enjoy!

It is as well to remember that to give ourselves the best chance of avoiding heart disease we not only require a healthy diet but to give up cigarette smoking and to take regular physical activity. That need not mean buying a tracksuit by the way, just regular walking at a reasonable pace for twenty-five minutes most days of the week will help.

You will find that Anne Lindsay's book contains recipes that will enable you to combine a healthy diet with all the joys of eating. Bon appetite!

Professor B L Pentecost MD FRCP
Medical Director
British Heart Foundation

FOR THE TIME OF YOUR LIFE

Most people want to live as well as possible, as long as possible. This cookbook has been designed to help you do just that.

Recent research into the cause of cardiovascular disease (heart-related ailments and stroke) shows that the health of your heart may be more in your control than you've realized. There appears to be a direct connection between what you eat and your chances of developing a heart condition or stroke.

The dietary changes recommended to give your heart its best chance are not drastic. If you follow the British Heart Foundation's recommendations, you'll be enjoying a wide variety of delicious foods, perhaps an even greater variety than you've enjoyed before.

The Light-Hearted Cookbook contains everything you need to know to put your healthy heart plan into action — menus, recipes, lifestyle tips for various age groups and some basic heart and nutrition information.

But before you start cooking, let's look at the scientific backdrop to this cookbook and the background for the British Heart Foundation's recommendations.

YOUR HEART AND YOU

Cardiovascular Disease — Britain's Number 1 Killer

This year alone, roughly 300,000 Britons will die of heart- and blood vessel-related ailments. Many more will suffer non-fatal heart attacks or strokes. Currently, several million British people suffer from some form of heart or blood vessel disease, many of them middle-aged or younger.

While these statistics are frightening, the picture is not as bad as it once was. In the last 10 years death rates for CHD in the UK for adults aged 16-64 have fallen by 41%. Increased public education, lifestyle changes and breakthroughs resulting from medical research have all contributed to the decline. But more and more, the role of the individual to change those habits that lead to cardiovascular disease is becoming increasingly important.

Defining a Complex Disease

The term "cardiovascular disease" includes all diseases of the heart and of the blood vessels that lead to various parts of the body. Two of the most common conditions, heart attack and stroke, are usually caused by narrowed blood vessels.

A heart attack occurs when there is an inadequate flow of blood to the heart muscle, while a stroke is usually caused by a lack of blood flow to the brain. The narrowing of the blood vessels leading to both the heart and brain, commonly referred to as hardening of the arteries, is caused by atherosclerosis.

How the arteries become narrowed over the years is that cholesterol, fat and calcium are deposited in the artery walls. It's like the accumulation of plaque on teeth, only the results are more serious. The arterial build-up makes it harder for the blood to pass through, and should a blockage occur, as a result of a blood clot or of fatty deposits breaking off from the arterial wall, a heart attack or stroke results.

Controlling the Risk

Over the years, scientists have identified a number of factors that increase your chances of developing heart disease. Some like heredity, you can do nothing about. But many of the major risk factors can be controlled, as you can see from these lists:

Uncontrollable Risk Factors	Potentially Controllable Factors
Family history of heart disease	Smoking
Gender	High blood pressure
Increasing age	High blood cholesterol
	Poor eating habits
	Excess weight or obesity
	Diabetes
	Excess alcohol
	Inactivity

As you can see, the factors that are within your control far outnumber the ones that aren't. In this book, the focus is on those you can change, with particular emphasis on those factors that involve diet. But to start with, here's a short list of changes you should consider.

Six Ways to a Healthier Heart
(1) Avoid smoking.
(2) Have your blood pressure checked regularly and have it treated if it is high.
(3) Be active at least five times a week, for a half hour each time.
(4) Maintain a healthy body weight.
(5) Limit your alcohol intake to 14 units a week (female), 21 units a week (male). A unit is a $\frac{1}{2}$ pt of normal strength beer or lager, a glass of wine or measure of spirits as served in a pub. This amount should be spread throughout the week leaving a couple of days alcohol-free.
(6) Eat a healthy diet based on The Food Guide (page 206).

THE FOOD FACTORS

Food plays a large part in the enjoyment of life, and as the previous list indicates, a large part in minimizing your risk of heart disease. Blood pressure, weight control, healthy arteries and blood cholesterol levels are all tied to diet.

If you've paid little attention to what you ate in the past, now is the time to take a hard look at your eating habits and make those changes that will help your heart. What are they? The following are the most recent British government's guidelines, fully endorsed by the British Heart Foundation.

The Eight Guidelines for a Healthy Diet
(1) Enjoy your food.
(2) Eat a variety of different foods.
(3) Eat the right amount to be a healthy weight.
(4) Eat plenty of foods rich in starch and fibre.
(5) Don't eat too much fat.
(6) Don't eat sugary foods too often.
(7) Look after the vitamins and minerals in your food.
(8) If you drink, keep within sensible limits.

There is strong evidence of a link between the amount of salt we have in our diet and our blood pressure levels. Cutting down salt intake has resulted in a lowered blood pressure. Therefore, it is recommended that we cut our salt intake to about 6g/day.

Working Out the Numbers
Recommendations are all very well, but what do they mean in practice? How do I know if I have to cut down my fat intake to less than 35% total food calories? What does 10% saturated fat look like. It may seem difficult to imagine how these figures work out in terms of what we eat. In the following pages, each of the recommendations is explored in more depth. *The Light-Hearted Cookbook* gives you examples of the amounts of fat, and calories, found in food. The recipes include that kind of information, too, and follow the British Heart Foundation's recommendations. Basically, what you should remember is:

– *LESS* **total fat and less saturated fat**
– *MORE* **fruit, vegetable, fish, and whole grain breads and cereals. Everyone should eat five or more pieces of fruit and vegetables every day.**

If you're a typical person, here's what you're currently consuming compared to what you should be eating.

	Current typical consumption	Recommended consumption
Carbohydrates	45% of calories	50% of calories
Fats	40% of calories	35% of calories
Saturated Fat	17% of calories	10% of calories

The following sections go through the dietary recommendations to explain why they are necessary and what you can do to bring your eating habits in line with healthy living.

Fat — the Major Factor

In a typical day, people consume 40 percent or more of their calories in the form of fats. That's almost one-third above the level considered to minimize the risk of cardiovascular disease.

Of course, a small amount of fat in the diet is needed and it is virtually impossible to have a fat free diet. An extremely low-fat diet is considered dangerous since fat performs many important functions in the body, like the transportation of some vitamins and the provision of essential fatty acids and energy. But most people go overboard. Here's where fat is found in the average diet:

Common Sources of Fat in the Diet

Meat and meat products	25%
Cereal products (Biscuits, cakes and puddings)	19%
Fat spreads	16%
Milk and milk products	15%
Vegetables including roast/fried potatoes/chips	11%
Other foods	14%

The Three Faces of Fat

All fats are not equal in their effect on blood cholesterol. Foods containing fats are made up of a variety of different kinds of fat. They are listed here under the kind of fat they are highest in.

Fat type	Form	Sources
Saturated	Usually solid at room temperature	Butter, lard, vegetable shortening, coconut oil, palm oil, highly hydrogenated margarines, or hydrogenated vegetable oils, fatty meat, cheese, dairy products, chocolate, coconut, non-milk fat
Monounsaturated	Liquid at room temperature	Rapeseed oil, sunflower oil, peanut oil, peanuts, peanut butter, cashews, avocado, some margarines and spreads
Polyunsaturated	Liquid at room temperature	Safflower oil, sunflower oil, corn oil, soyabean oil, some margarines and spreads, fish, almonds, hazelnuts

Separating the "Good" from the "Bad" Cholesterol

All fats, including cholesterol, are transported through the body in the form of lipoproteins, which are a combination of fat and protein and can be considered "good" or "bad".

High-Density Lipoproteins — The "Good"

HDL's are relatively durable fat-carrying protein compounds that actually carry excess cholesterol to the liver for processing and elimination from the body.

Low-Density Lipoproteins — The "Bad"
LDL's are less stable and more likely to break apart and to deposit cholesterol in the blood vessels, which can lead to atherosclerosis. Most people with high blood cholesterol levels also have high LDL levels.

Accentuate the Positive
The higher the HDL, the better your chances of arterial health. There are a number of steps you can take to raise your level of HDL's.
– Be more active.
– Keep your weight at a healthy level (overweight people are more likely to have higher levels of LDL's).
– Don't smoke.
– Reduce your intake of saturated fat.

The most effective dietary measure in reducing blood cholesterol is to reduce saturated fat. In everyday living the best way to do this is to reduce your total fat intake.

The British Heart Foundation recommends that no more than 10% of your calorie intake comes from saturated fat and the remaining fat intake from monosaturated and polyunsaturated fat to make up to no more than 35% of daily calories.

Good News about Monounsaturated and Polyunsaturated Fats
Research indicates that monounsaturated fats, such as olive or rapeseed oils can help reduce blood cholesterol levels, while retaining the protective HDL cholesterol levels.

Polyunsaturated fats, such as safflower oil, help to decrease blood-cholesterol levels, and some recent research indicates that some monounsaturated fats, such as olive or rapeseed oils may do the same thing.

Developments in heart research show that one type of polyunsaturated fat, the Omega 3 fatty acid from fish oils help to prevent atherosclerosis. Omega 3 fatty acids are found in oily fish such as salmon, sardines, pilchards, trout, mackerel, tuna and herring. (Canned tuna fish is not actually rich in Omega 3 fatty acids but as a tasty and low fat alternative to meat and cheese, is a good food for the family). These Omega 3 fatty acids also help lower blood fat in the form of triglycerides. They also make the blood less sticky, thereby less susceptible to the risk of blood clots.

The British Heart Foundation doesn't recommend that you take fish oil supplements at this time. But eating fish two or three times a week is considered a healthy investment in the future.

Cutting Out Dietary Cholesterol
An issue related to fat is dietary cholesterol, a fatty substance the body needs in small amounts. The problem with cholesterol is that your liver will produce it, even if you eat no cholesterol in your food. A high level of blood cholesterol has been identified as a major risk factor in heart disease. You can do very little

about the amount of cholesterol your body produces, but most people can lower blood cholesterol by limiting the amount of fat, particularly saturated fat in their diet. For most people, however, there is no need to worry about foods which have a high cholesterol content, provided they are low in fat.

The three particular types of food which may concern or confuse you are eggs, offal (eg, liver, kidney) and shellfish (eg, prawns, shrimps). These foods are all quite low in fat but contain significant amounts of dietary cholesterol.

Providing your total intake is low (70 g for women and 100 g for men, see page 67) you can safely eat 4–6 eggs a week and both offal and shellfish once a week.

So, to summarise — the best way of looking after your *blood* cholesterol level is to cut down on total fat and particularly saturated fat. Don't worry about *dietary* cholesterol — providing your diet is low in fat, the *blood* cholesterol should take care of itself.

If you are at particular risk of Coronary Heart Disease your doctor will check your blood cholesterol level for you.

Butter Versus Margarine
Both butter and margarine are fats, but butter is high in saturated fat and should be avoided. Instead use a margarine labelled high in monosaturates or polyunsaturates, or a low fat spread from the recommended list on page 208. For cooking, try an oil that is low in saturated fat.

Hydrogenation is a process used to turn a liquid oil into a solid fat. It is used in the production of most margarines so that the oil-based product can be spread at room temperature. But as a result of the hydrogenation process, an unsaturated vegetable oil becomes more saturated.

Not all margarines have the same degree of hydrogenation. In most cases, the harder the margarine, the more hydrogenated and more saturated it will be. The British Heart Foundation recommends that you use those margarines subjected to the least degree of hydrogenation, so that they are lower in saturated fat and higher in polyunsaturated or monounsaturated fat.

To sort out margarines for yourself, read the labels. Look for those that claim to be 'High in Polyunsaturates' or simply 'High in Unsaturates'. (See page 208 for Recommended Margarines.)

Compare:	g total fat per 1 tbsp (15 ml)	g saturated fat per 1 tbsp (15 ml)
Butter	12	8
Hard or soft margarine	12	4
Sunflower margarine	12	2
Low-fat spread	6	1

Estimating Fat

The suggested menus and recipes in this book are all relatively low in fat and give the grams of fat per serving.

For this to be meaningful look at the chart that follows to see how many grams of fat you need in a day to follow the 35 percent of calories guideline. (See page 212 for a height, weight and corresponding calorie recommended intake table.)

Calorie intake/day	Grams fat/day to equal 35% of calories
1200	47
1800	70
2200	85
2500	97
3000	117
3200	124

If you follow a Food Selection Guide, choosing the low-fat foods within each food group, and limiting the fat used in preparing these foods, you'll probably meet that goal.

Safety Switch — to Reduce Fats

Choose	Instead of	Grams of fat saved
1 glass fully skimmed milk	1 glass whole milk	9
1 oz (25 g) grated Edam, mozzarella or low-fat cheese	1 oz (25 g) grated Cheddar cheese	5
2 oz (50 g) cottage cheese	2 oz (50 g) cream cheese	20
4 oz (120 g) chicken, no skin	4 oz (120 g) chicken, with skin	6
Bread with 1 tsp (5 ml) margarine	Bread with 2 tsp (10 ml) margarine	4
Salad, 1 tbsp (15 ml) low-fat mayonnaise	Salad, 1 tbsp (15 ml) mayonnaise	6
1 pear or tomato	1 avocado	30
Apple crisp (page 167)	Apple pie	13
Wholemeal bun	Rich Fruit Cake	8

Trimming the Fat

– Use as little butter, margarine and oil as possible (where possible use a highly unsaturated or low-fat spread) on toast, sandwiches, vegetables and, especially, in cooking. Use lemon juice or herbs on vegetables instead of butter.
– Instead of frying, try the low-fat cooking methods — grilling, baking, steaming, poaching and boiling.
– Roast meats on a rack and sauté in a nonstick pan. Sauté vegetables in 1 tsp (5 ml) oil and 2 fl oz (60 ml) water.
– After browning meat, spoon off all the fat.

- Trim the visible fat from meat and remove the skin from poultry. Choose lean cuts and watch serving sizes of meat, too. Three or four ounces (80 to 100 g), about the size of a pack of cards, is a good portion.
- Keep salad dressings to a minimum and switch to oil-free dressings, low-fat mayonnaise or salad cream.
- Serve low-fat relishes and sauces, like cranberry or mint sauce, with meat, rather than rich sauces or gravies.
- Substitute fully or semi-skimmed for whole milk and opt for other low-fat dairy products — low-fat cheese, light soured cream, low-fat yogurt, fromage frais.
- Snack on fresh fuits, vegetables and unbuttered popcorn; avoid crisps, peanuts, chips, rich desserts, whipped cream.

Salt — Licking the Habit

Everyone thinks it makes peanuts taste better, but people may not be aware that excessive salt may lead to hypertension, coronary heart disease, a stroke or kidney failure.

The problem with salt is that there's a lot around you don't see. It's in processed foods, sauces, snack foods and many other surprising items.

Here's how you might try cutting down on your salt intake.

Salt Shakers
- The taste for salt is acquired and can be un-acquired. Think about the salt you use and always taste *before* you add salt, gradually decreasing the amount.
- Don't automatically add salt to cooking water. Add it, if necessary, after tasting, just before serving.
- Take the salt pot off the table or use a pepper pot for the salt (smaller holes) instead.
- Season foods with lemon juice, vinegar, a pinch of sugar, mustard, herbs, spices, peppers, ginger, garlic, onion or wine instead of salt.
- Watch out for such high salt foods as processed luncheon meats, bacon, sausages, smoked meats or fish, potato crisps, pretzels, salted crackers, pickles, soya sauce, MSG (Monosodiumglutamate), canned or dried soups and processed cheese.
- Read labels and avoid sodium compounds as well as salt, if you can. For example, MSG is very high in sodium.

Because everyone's taste for salt varies and we hope you will gradually reduce your taste for salt, most of the recipes in this book call for no salt or salt to taste, and have been tested without any or using a minimum of salt.Occasionally, comparisons (measured in mg sodium) are given to show what a benefit cooking your own recipes can be.

Generally speaking, foods made from scratch are better for you than processed or convenience foods, because *you* can control the amount of fat, salt and other ingredients.

Sugar — Sweet Surrender

The average person consumes about $1\frac{1}{2}$ pounds of sugar a week, enough to make your fillings ache. The problem is not only the sugar you eat directly in desserts or tea and coffee, but the hidden sugar in prepared foods, from cereal to confectionary, cakes and fizzy drinks. Sugar is a simple carbohydrate that supplies energy to the body but little else in the way of nutrition. The high calorie count in sugar-containing foods can lead to weight gain, one of the risk factors in heart disease. Also, if you are consuming a lot of sugar, you may be missing out on more nutritious foods, especially good snack foods like fruit, raw vegetables and whole grains.

To kick the sugar habit, see the tips in the shopping section on pages 199–200 and the recipe modification section for desserts and baked goods on page 144.

Fibre — Naturally Right

Fibre is a substance in food that is not digested or is partially digested. Your grandparents called it roughage and knew it helped keep them regular. Now there is growing evidence that certain types of fibre, such as in oat bran, may help lower blood cholesterol, as well. Fibre may also help protect the body against certain types of cancer, particularly colorectal cancer.

To increase your fibre intake, eat more fruits, vegetables, especially pulse vegetables like beans, peas and lentils and whole grain breads and cereals. Be sure to include a variety, since different types of fibre perform different functions in the body. As a bonus, fibre-rich foods are nutritious and are usually low in calories and fat too. A complete list of fibre-rich foods is on page 207.

How much is enough? It is recommended that healthy Britons should eat half as much again as their current intake of dietary fibre from a variety of foods. Fibre supplements are not recommended. Too much fibre isn't healthy either, as food then passes through the intestines too quickly and some vitamins and minerals will not be absorbed. It's important to increase fibre levels slowly, so that you don't suffer any discomfort. The recipe section of this book also includes suggestions for fibre.

Tips for Increasing the Fibre in Your Diet:
– Have at least five servings of fruit and vegetables a day.
– Eat pulse vegetables such as beans, peas and lentils as a
   substitute for some meats as they are high in protein, low in fat
   and very high in fibre.
– Add chick peas or kidney beans to soups, salads, casseroles.
– Eat the edible skins of fruits and vegetables and choose whole
   fruits instead of juices.
– Use wholemeal flour. In most recipes you can substitute half
   of the plain flour with wholemeal flour.
– Choose whole wheat foods when buying bread, pasta,
   muffins, spaghetti, pitta bread, hamburger buns, crackers.
– Add dried fruits (prunes, raisins) and nuts to your cereals; use
   them to top fruit or ice cream desserts.
– Have fruits and vegetables for snacks as well as in meals.
– Choose breakfast cereals with at least 2 grams fibre per
   serving.

Safety Switch — to Increase Fibre

Choose	Instead of
Fresh orange	Orange juice
Wholemeal bread	White bread
Cereals with 2 grams or more fibre/serving	Cereals with less than 2 grams fibre/serving
Wholemeal bun	White bun
Chilli	Hot dog
Lentil or bean soup	Cream soup
Canned baked beans	Canned pasta
Spinach salad	Iceberg lettuce salad
Potato with skin	Potato without skin
Raw vegetables and dip	Crisps and dip
Fruit-based desserts	Puddings, pastries

THE LIFESTYLE FACTORS

Good food alone will not keep your heart healthy. There are a few other adjustments you may need to make in your life.

Smoking — Butt Out
To put it bluntly, don't smoke. If you smoke a pack of cigarettes a day, your risk of a heart attack doubles. Smoke even more and your risk rises higher. Smoking is probably the single most preventable cause of heart disease.

Physical Activity – Get Moving
Modern conveniences make it easy to lead a fairly sedentary existence. Unless you plan for exercise, you might not get it. Yet moderate exercise can greatly reduce your risk of heart disease – by halving your risk of hypertension, by lowering your blood cholesterol level, by controlling your weight and your stress level.

Aerobic exercise, such as running, walking, swimming and cycling, increases the body's ability to use oxygen and strengthens the heart muscle. Try for at least five 30-minute periods of physical activity per week.

Alcohol — Hold Out
Excess alcohol consumption can damage your body in many ways, including increasing your risk of heart disease. Alcohol can prevent your body from absorbing important nutrients. If you drink, try to limit your consumption to 14 units a week (female), 21 units (male). See also page 2.

IN GOOD COMPANY

Many of the recommendations of the British Heart Foundation are shared by other health organizations, like 'Europe Against Cancer' which also suggests limiting total fat, increasing your fibre intake and eating more fruit and vegetables. Because diabetes is also a risk factor in heart disease, it is an added reason for diabetics to follow the British Heart Foundation's guidelines — and the good news is that the recommendations are the same; less fat, more fibre and watch your weight.

What this means to you is that the good food practices given here are recommended by a wide variety of health professionals. Eating for a healthy heart means eating for a better chance of overall health. And that means eating for a better, and perhaps longer, life for you and your family.

Microwave Note

Recipes have been tested in a 700-watt full-size microwave oven with a turntable. If your oven is different, cooking times may have to be adjusted slightly. If you don't have a turntable you may have to rotate dishes once or twice during cooking.

SAMPLE DAILY MENU PLANS

The following menus do not exceed 2000 calories per day and follow the British Heart Foundation's recommendations; their fat content does not exceed 35 percent of the total calories. People who need to eat more than 2000 calories should follow these menus, simply increasing the portions by the appropriate amount to meet their energy needs.

Recipes for dishes noted with asterisks appear in this book and can be found by using the index.

Menu 1	Sample Daily Menu with a Restaurant Lunch	
% of Calories from Fat = 28%	g fat	calories
Breakfast		
Melon or Grapefruit ($\frac{1}{2}$)	Trace	93
Slice Wholemeal and Oatmeal Bread (1)*	5	176
Fruit-flavoured low-fat yogurt (5 oz [125 g])	2	131
Restaurant lunch		
Apple juice ($\frac{1}{4}$ pt [150 ml])	Trace	62
Sliced chicken sandwich (sliced chicken from $\frac{1}{2}$ breast, lettuce, 2 slices bread, and 1 tsp mayonnaise)	5	313
Tossed green salad with oil and vinegar dressing (1 tsp oil and 3 tsp [15 ml] vinegar)	5	56
Semi-skimmed milk ($\frac{1}{2}$ pt [300 ml])	5	128
Dinner		
Mexican Rice and Bean Casserole*	5	275
Broccoli spears (4 oz [100 g])	Trace	48
Spinach Salad with Sesame Seed Dressing*	9	116
Slice toast (1)	Trace	76
Unsaturated margarine (2 tsp [10 ml] — for broccoli and toast)	8	66
Semi-skimmed milk ($\frac{1}{2}$ pt [300 ml])	5	128
Applesauce and Raisin Squares*	3	73
Totals	52	1741

*Recipes included in this book.

Menu 2	Sample Daily Menu with a Packed Lunch	
% of Calories from Fat = 26%	g fat	calories
Breakfast		
Orange juice (¼ pt [150 ml])	Trace	59
Whole-wheat cereal — Shreddies (2 oz [50 g])	Trace	165
Sliced banana (1)	Trace	105
Slice toast (1)	Trace	76
Unsaturated margarine (1 tsp [5 ml])	4	33
Semi-skimmed milk (½ pt [300 ml])	5	128
Packed Lunch		
Gouda cheese (1½ oz [40 g])	13	164
Crusty roll (1)	2	200
Unsaturated margarine (1 tsp [5 ml])	4	33
Carrot and celery sticks	Trace	37
Easy Oat Bran and Date Biscuit* (1)	4	97
Apple juice (¼ pt [150 ml])	Trace	62
Dinner		
Linguine with Salmon and Chives*	12	400
Tossed Seasonal Greens*	2	30
Roll (1)	2	156
Unsaturated margarine (1 tsp [5 ml])	4	33
Pineapple and Orange Sorbet*	Trace	93
Semi-skimmed milk (½ pt [300 ml])	5	128
Totals	57	1999

*Recipes included in this book.

Menu 3	Sample Daily Menu with Lunch at Home	
% of Calories from Fat = 27%	g fat	calories
Breakfast		
Grapefruit ($\frac{1}{2}$)	Trace	39
Bran flakes (2 oz [50 g])	Trace	139
Slice wholemeal toast (1)	Trace	61
Peanut butter (1 tbsp [15 ml])	8	95
Semi-skimmed milk ($\frac{1}{2}$ pt [300 ml])	5	128
Lunch at home		
Pasta and Fresh Vegetable Salad*	6	165
Tuna fish (4 oz [100 g]) (canned in brine)	1	135
Roll (1)	2	156
Unsaturated margarine (1 tsp [5 ml])	4	33
Semi-skimmed milk ($\frac{1}{2}$ pt [300 ml])	5	128
Dinner		
Pork Chops with Rosemary and Orange*	9	201
Garlic and Parsley Potatoes*	2	119
Stir-Fry Ratatouille*	7	107
Grated Carrot and Green Pea Salad*	1	71
Sliced Peaches (6 oz [150 g])	Trace	115
Plain biscuits (2)	2	57
Totals	52	1749

*Recipes included in this book.

Menu 4	Sample Daily Menu with a Packed Lunch	
% of Calories from Fat = 23%	g fat	calories
Breakfast		
Orange slices (1 orange)	Trace	62
Slices toast (2)	Trace	152
Edam or low-fat cheese (1 oz [25 g])	5	71
Unsaturated margarine (1 tsp [5 ml]) plus honey, jam or marmalade	4	83
Packed Lunch		
Classic Tuna Salad with Fresh Dill sandwich*	5	238
Cucumber slices (3 oz [75 g])	Trace	7
Pear	Trace	100
Semi-skimmed milk ($\frac{1}{2}$ pt [300 ml])	5	128
Apple Cake*	5	174
Dinner		
6 oz (150 g) Grilled Tandoori Chicken* with rice (8 oz [200 g])	14	440
Green beans (4 oz [100 g])	Trace	46
Winter Fruit Compôte with Figs and Apricots (one serving)*	1	148
Semi-skimmed milk ($\frac{1}{2}$ pt [300 ml])	5	128
Totals	44	1777

*Recipes included in this book.

DAILY TOTAL PROTEIN, FAT AND CARBOHYDRATE INTAKE ACCORDING TO PERCENTAGE OF
TOTAL CALORIES ACCORDING TO BRITISH HEART FOUNDATION'S DIETARY
RECOMMENDATIONS

Energy Intake Calories (kjoules)	% calories from protein	grams protein per day	% calories from fat	grams fat per day	% calories from carbohydrate	grams carbohydrate per day
1200 (5040)	15	45	35	47	55	165
1500 (6300)	15	56	35	58	55	206
1800 (7560)	15	68	35	70	55	248
2100 (8820)	15	79	35	82	55	289
2300 (9660)	15	86	35	89	55	316
2600 (11,172)	15	98	35	101	55	357
2900 (12,180)	15	109	35	113	55	399
3200 (13,440)	15	120	35	124	55	440

NB
The total energy intake from food can be measured in either kilo calories (usually shortened to kcal and described as 'Calories') or the modern SI. unit, kilojoules. The multiplication factor is 4.2; hence a 2000 kcal diet is 8400 kjoules (or 8.4 mega joules).

A slice of bread, containing approximately 100 kcal would equate to 420 kjoules.

APPETIZERS AND SNACKS

An appetizer or starter makes a meal more special. Appetizers are my favourite part of restaurant meals; I will often pass on dessert in favour of an interesting salad or soup and will sometimes order two appetizers rather than a main course.

Some starters or hors d'oeuvres, such as meat or chicken liver pâtés and creamy cheeses, can be terribly high in fat and calories and can quickly add to our daily intake. On the other hand, there are many terrific-tasting starters that aren't too heavy in calories — try the Prawn Mousse with Dill or Spiced Meatballs with Coriander Dip or others in this section, or any of the soup or salad recipes for starters, which your family and guests will ask for again and again.

Salmon Spread with Capers

I keep a tin of salmon on the shelf and a bottle of capers in the refrigerator in case someone drops in unexpectedly. Then I can make this in a few seconds to serve as a spread with crackers or pitta bread, or use to stuff vegetables, such as cherry tomatoes or mange tout. Spring onions, chives, sweet peppers or fresh dill can be used instead of celery. Choose sockeye salmon for its bright red colour.

PER 1 tbsp (15 ml) SERVING	
calories	17
g fat	1
g protein	2
g carbohydrate	0

7½ oz	tin salmon	213 g
1 oz	capers, drained	25 g
1 oz	finely chopped celery	25 g
2 tbsp	low-fat natural yogurt	30 m
1 tsp	lemon juice	5 m
	hot pepper sauce	
2 tbsp	chopped fresh parsley	30 m

Nutrition Note
Be sure to crush salmon bones and include them as they are an excellent source of calcium; also include the juices because they contain omega 3 fatty acids, which may help in reducing the risk of heart disease.

In a small bowl, flake salmon along with juices and well-mashed bones. Add capers, celery, yogurt and lemon juice; mix well. Add hot pepper sauce to taste. Spoon into serving bowl and sprinkle with parsley. Makes 10 fl oz (300 ml).

Spinach and Onion Dip

PER 1 tbsp (15 ml) SERVING (made with low-fat natural yogurt)	
calories	10
fat	0
g protein	1
g carbohydrate	1

Variations

Parsley and Onion Dip
Instead of spinach, substitute 1 oz (25 g) coarsely chopped fresh parsley.

Fresh Basil and Onion Dip
Instead of spinach, substitute 1 oz (25 g) coarsely chopped fresh basil leaves.

Dill Dip
Instead of spinach, substitute ⅓ oz (10 g) coarsely chopped fresh parsley and ⅔ oz (20 g) chopped fresh dill (or 1 tbsp [15 ml] dried dillweed).

Prawn, Crab or Clam Dip
Instead of spinach, add 5 oz (142 g) can drained rinsed crab, small prawns or clams.

Curry Dip
Instead of spinach, add 1 tsp (5 ml) each curry powder and ground cumin; mix well then season with more to taste.

*Instead of low-fat cottage cheese, dip is made with 9 oz (230 g) of ingredients listed.
**Although cream cheese is lower in total fat than mayonnaise, it is not recommended because it is higher in saturated fat.

This is a good creamy yet low-fat base for many dips. Instead of spinach, you can add other vegetables, herbs or seasonings (see Variations). Serve this dip surrounded with fresh, crisp vegetables, such as carrots, celery, sweet peppers, asparagus, broccoli or cauliflower. It's best to make it at least four hours in advance so that flavours can develop.

10 oz	fresh spinach (or frozen chopped, thawed)	300 g
9 oz	low-fat cottage cheese	230 g
1 tbsp	lemon juice	15 ml
5 oz	low-fat natural yogurt	120 g
½ oz	chopped fresh parsley	15 g
1 oz	chopped spring onion	25 g
1 tsp	salt	5 ml
	freshly ground pepper	

Trim stems and coarse leaves from spinach. Wash spinach, cook, covered, over medium heat for 3 minutes or until wilted. (If using frozen, no need to cook.)

Thoroughly drain, squeezing out excess moisture; coarsely chop and set aside.

In blender or food processor, process cottage cheese with lemon juice until blended. Add spinach, yogurt, parsley, onion, salt, and pepper to taste; process just until mixed.

Cover and refrigerate for at least 4 hours or overnight to blend flavours. Makes approximately 1pt (600 ml).

Compare: Many dips are made with mayonnaise or cream cheese as a base; these are much higher in fat and calories. Just as good-tasting, if not better, dips can be made using cottage cheesse and/or yogurt.

Spinach and Onion Dip*		
9 oz (230 g)	g fat	calories
Low-fat yogurt	4	158
Cottage cheese	5	214
Light sour cream	13	220
Sour cream	46	475
Low-calorie mayonnaise	80	928
Mayonnaise	176	1632
Cream cheese**	80	832

Broccoli and Mushroom Dip

Chopped broccoli adds colour, flavour and fibre to this low-calorie dip.

PER 1 tbsp (15 ml) SERVING (made with low-fat natural yogurt)	
calories	12
g fat	0.5
g protein	1
g carbohydrate	1

8 oz	chopped broccoli (include stalks)	225
1 tbsp	unsaturated vegetable oil	15 m
1	clove garlic, crushed	
$\frac{1}{2}$	onion, chopped	
$\frac{1}{4}$ lb	mushrooms, coarsely chopped	125
8 oz	low-fat cottage cheese	200
$2\frac{1}{2}$ oz	low-fat natural yogurt	60
	salt and freshly ground pepper	

In pot of boiling water, cook broccoli just until tender-crisp (3 minutes). Drain and refresh under cold water; drain again and set aside.

In nonstick pan, heat oil over medium heat; add garlic, onion and mushrooms and cook, shaking pan to prevent sticking, for minutes or until onion is tender. Set aside.

In food processor, combine cottage cheese and yogurt; process until smooth. Add mushroom mixture and broccoli; season with salt and pepper to taste. Process with on/off motion just until mixed. Cover and refrigerate for up to 2 days. Makes approximately 1 pt (600 ml).

Crackers

When buying crackers it pays to spend a few minutes reading the labels. Many crackers are high in salt and contain hydrogenated vegetable oil (palm or coconut), which means they have saturated fat.

Melba toast and crispbreads are two kinds of crackers without hydrogenated vegetable oil.

For dips and spreads, instead of crackers use raw vegetables, wholemeal pitta bread rounds (tear into smaller pieces) or Low-Salt Bagel Thins (page 21) and Quick Homemade Melba Toast (page 20).

Raw Veggies for Snacks

If you keep a supply of cut-up celery and carrots, broccoli or cauliflower in the refrigerator they will often be chosen for snacks over biscuits and crisps.

However, if you store them in a bowl of water, they will lose most of their vitamin C; instead, store them in a plastic bag with a few drops of water.

PER 1 tbsp (15 ml) SERVING	
calories	12
g fat	0.5
g protein	1.5
g carbohydrate	0.5

**To Unmould Prawn Mousse
with Dill**
Run a knife around mousse to
loosen from mould. Invert
onto serving platter. Cover
with hot, damp tea towel for 1
minute. Hold mould and
platter securely and give a
strong shake to release
mousse. Remove mould.

Prawn Mousse with Dill

Serve as part of a light salad, or surround with crackers, Melba
toast or fresh vegetables for a delicious appetizer spread.
(Recipe pictured opposite page 24).

1	leaf gelatine	1
4 fl oz	cold water	125 ml
2 oz	spring onions or chives, finely chopped	50 g
1 oz	chopped fresh dill	25 g
1 tbsp	lemon juice	15 ml
$\frac{1}{2}$ tsp	salt	2 ml
$\frac{1}{2}$ tsp	granulated sugar	2 ml
Dash	hot pepper sauce	Dash
2 tbsp	tomato purée	30 ml
9 oz	low-fat natural yogurt	230 g
6 oz	sour cream	150 g
2 oz	finely chopped celery	50 g
12 oz	small cooked prawns, coarsely chopped	375 g
	fresh dill	

In microwave-safe bowl or small saucepan, sprinkle gelatine
over cold water; let stand until softened, about 5 minutes.
Microwave at high (100%) power for 40 seconds or warm over
medium heat until gelatine is dissolved; let cool slightly.

In bowl combine onions, dill, lemon juice, salt, sugar, hot
pepper sauce, tomato purée, yogurt, sour cream, celery and
gelatine; mix well. Stir in prawn and refrigerate until mixture
begins to set. Spoon into lightly oiled $1\frac{1}{2}$ pt (1 litre) mould or,
alternatively, spoon into serving bowl. Cover and refrigerate
until firm, at least 3 hours.

Unmould onto serving plate or serve in bowl and garnish with
sprigs of fresh dill. Makes approximately $1\frac{1}{2}$ pt (1 litre).

Appetizer or First Course

When planning menus try to make sure each course has different foods and that the whole meal is a pleasing combination of colours, textures, seasonings, flavours and temperature. If you have a filling first course such as Fettuccine and Mussel Salad, plan a light main course of perhaps a fish and a green vegetable. If you have a main course that is high in fat and calories choose a light first course such as a soup without cream.

As well as the recipes in this section consider a soup, salad, pasta or fish for a first course.

Homemade Tortilla Chips

These are a healthy alternative to shop-bought tortilla chips, which are high in calories, fat and salt. Use fresh, frozen or canned tortillas (whole wheat if you can find them) for these crisp easy-to-make chips.

Dip each tortilla in water; drain off excess. Cut into 6 wedges and place on baking sheet. Bake in 475° (240°C) Gas Mark 9 oven for 6 minutes. Let cool and store in airtight container for up to 2 weeks. (1 oz [25 g] of chips has about 1 g fat, 62 calories.)

Compare: This type of spread is often made with mayonnaise and whipping cream. I prefer a lighter version made with yogurt and sour cream.

Prawn Mousse with Dill

per 2 fl oz (60 ml)	g fat	calories
Made with: yogurt and sour cream (low fat)	2	48
or with: mayonnaise (4 oz [100 g]) and whipping cream (6 oz [150 g])	8	108

Quick Homemade Melba Toast

Choose fine-grained bread such as wholemeal or white sliced loaf. Cut in very thin slices (remove crusts if you want) and arrange in a single layer on a baking sheet. Bake in 250°F (120°C) Gas Mark ½ oven for 20 to 30 minutes or until crisp. Time will vary depending on how old the bread and how thick the slices.

Snacks and Nibbles

These can quickly add up to a great deal of fat and calories. For example, if you consume about 2000 calories a day you should have no more than 78 grams of fat.

High-Fat Snacks	g fat
Peanuts (2½ oz [70 g])	35
Potato crisps (1 small bag [30 g])	11
Cheddar cheese (1½ oz [45 g], a 2 inch[5 cm] cube)	15

Lower-Fat Alternative Snacks	g fat
Prawn Mousse with Dill (2 fl oz [60 ml]) (page 19)	2
Low fat Cheddar cheese (1½ oz [45 g])	3
Fresh Vegetables with Spinach and Onion Dip (page 17)	trace

Low-Salt Bagel Thins

If you love crisp, salty snacks such as potato crisps, here is a healthy alternative. How good they are depends on how thin you can slice the bagel.

1	bagel	1
2 tsp	soft unsaturated margarine, melted	10 ml
1 tsp	dried oregano	5 ml

Using very sharp serrated knife, slice bagel into very thin rounds. Arrange in single layer on baking sheet; brush with margarine. Sprinkle with oregano. Bake in 350°F (180°C) Gas Mark 4 oven for 12 minutes. Let cool and store in airtight container for up to 1 week. Makes 20 pieces.

PER 1-piece SERVING	
calories	14
g fat	0.5
g protein	0
g carbohydrate	2

Italian Tomato Bruschetta

Traditionally, this Italian-style garlic bread is made by toasting thick slices of Italian bread, then rubbing them with a cut clove of garlic and drizzling with a top-quality, first-pressed olive oil. Sometimes the toast is topped with diced tomato or cheese. Here's a low-calorie, low-fat version that is equally delicious. Serve for a first course or as a snack, as an hors d'oeuvre on tiny toasted bread rounds or as part of a soup-and-salad meal.

8	slices French or Italian bread, ½ in (1 cm) thick	8
2	cloves garlic, halved	2
1 tsp	olive oil	5 ml
2 tbsp	onion, finely chopped	30 ml
1	large tomato, diced	1
Pinch	dried oregano	Pinch
Pinch	freshly ground pepper	Pinch
2 tsp	freshly grated Parmesan cheese (optional)	10 ml

To prepare Italian Tomato Bruschetta for a group, use the round Italian bread. Cut in half horizontally; prepare, and then cut into wedges to serve.

Anytime Snack

Italian Tomato Bruschetta (page 21)
Blackcurrant Cream Flan (page 155)

PER SERVING (including Parmesan)	
calories	105
g fat	2
g protein	3
g carbohydrate	19

Toast bread on both sides until brown. Rub one side of hot toast with cut side of garlic.

While bread is toasting, heat oil in nonstick pan over

Mussels aren't nearly as high
in cholesterol as previously
thought; about 3½ oz (90 g) of
mussels (meat only) has 50 mg
cholesterol.

medium-high heat; add onion and cook, stirring, until tender.
Add tomato, oregano and pepper; stir to mix.

Spoon tomato mixture over garlic side of hot toast and serve
immediately. Alternatively, sprinkle with Parmesan and (if
using) grill for 1 minute. Makes 4 servings (2 slices each).

Mussels on the Half Shell

These mussels look great on a hors d'oeuvre platter, aren't
difficult to make and are inexpensive compared to crab or
prawns.

3 lb	mussels	1.5 kg
2 fl oz	white wine or water	60 ml
2 tbsp	vegetable oil	30 ml
2 tbsp	lemon juice	30 ml
3	cloves garlic, finely chopped	3
¾ oz	chopped fresh parsley	20 g
2	medium tomatoes, diced	2

Scrub mussels and discard any that do not close when tapped;
cut off any hairy beards. In large heavy saucepan, bring wine or
water to boil. Add mussels, cover and cook over medium-high
heat for 5 to 7 minutes or until mussels open. Discard any that
do not open.

Remove from heat; reserve 2 tbsp (30 ml) of cooking liquid.
When mussels are cool enough to handle, using small knife,
separate mussels from shell and set aside; reserve half the shells.

In bowl, combine reserved cooking liquid, oil, lemon juice,
garlic, parsley and tomatoes; add mussels and stir gently. Cover
and refrigerate for 3 hours.

To serve, place a mussel in each half shell; spoon tomato
mixture over. Arrange on a platter and pass with drinks, or
arrange on individual plates and serve as first course.

Makes about 6 first-course servings or 50 to 60 pieces.

PER SERVING (9 mussels)		PER PIECE	
calories	114	calories	12
g fat	6	g fat	0.5
g protein	10	g protein	1
g carbohydrate	5	g carbohydrate	0.5
Good: vitamin C, iron, niacin			

Green Bean Appetizer Salad with Fresh Tomato and Chive Dressing

Serve this as a light first course in the summer and early autumn when green beans and tomatoes are at their sweetest and best flavour. It's also a great way to use up any leftover cooked beans.

Line salad plates with leaf lettuce. Arrange crisp-cooked and chilled beans and sliced raw mushrooms over lettuce. Spoon Fresh Tomato Chive Dressing (page 61) over beans (sprinkle feta cheese on top if not already added to dressing). Garnish with lemon wedges or chopped fresh herbs such as coriander, dill or basil.

PER SERVING (1 meatball)	
calories	28
g fat	1
g protein	2
g carbohydrate	2

Bake rather than fry meatballs; not only is there less fat as a result, it's also much easier.

Spiced Meatballs with Coriander Dip

Middle Eastern seasonings of cinnamon, allspice and garlic, plus crunchy water chestnuts and juicy raisins, make these meatballs the best I've tasted; salt will never be missed. Fresh coriander is available at some supermarkets and most Oriental grocery stores. Don't substitute the dried coriander; instead add curry powder to taste.

Meatballs

1½ oz	raisins	40 g
8 oz	lean minced lamb	200 g
3 oz	water chestnuts, finely chopped	75 g
2 tbsp	spring onions, finely chopped	30 ml
1	clove garlic, finely chopped	1
½ tsp	ground allspice	2 ml
½ tsp	cinnamon	2 ml
	freshly ground pepper	

Coriander Dip

9 oz	low-fat natural yogurt	230 g
3 tbsp	fresh coriander leaves, finely chopped	45 ml
	freshly ground pepper	

Meatballs: Soak raisins in hot water for 15 minutes; drain and chop. In bowl, combine raisins, lamb, water chestnuts, onions, garlic, allspice, cinnamon and pepper to taste; mix well.

Shape into 25 bite-size balls. Arrange in single layer in ungreased baking dish. Bake, uncovered, in 400°F (200°C) Gas Mark 6 oven for 20 minutes.

Coriander Dip: Meanwhile, in small bowl combine yogurt, coriander, and pepper to taste; cover and refrigerate for at least 30 minutes for flavours to develop. Serve hot meatballs with toothpicks for dipping into sauce.

Seafood Lettuce Rolls

These surprise packages are an intriguing and delicious first course. Serve with Coriander Dip (page 23).

PER SERVING	
calories	138
g fat	6
g protein	17
g carbohydrate	3
Good: calcium	
Excellent: niacin	

1	lettuce	1
7½ oz	tin salmon	213 g
1	dried red chilli pepper or 1 fresh hot pepper	1
5 oz	low-fat natural yogurt	120 g
8 oz	small cooked prawns	200 g
3 oz	alfalfa sprouts	75 g
	fresh coriander leaves (optional)	

If you enjoy Vietnamese cooking, serve the lettuce rolls with a nuoc cham dip and include rice vermicelli noodles in rolls. Thin strips of cooked pork can be used instead of salmon.

Nuoc Cham Dip
Split 2 dried chilli peppers in half and discard seeds and membranes; chop finely. In small dish combine peppers, 1 clove minced garlic, 1 tbsp (15 ml) granulated sugar, 1 tbsp (15 ml) lime juice, 3 tbsp (45 ml) water and 2 tbsp (30 ml) bottled fish sauce (available in Oriental food stores).

Cut large lettuce leaves in half down centre vein. In bowl, flake salmon along with juices and well-mashed bones. Split chilli pepper in half lengthwise, discard seeds and vein; finely chop and mix into yogurt.

On narrow end of each lettuce piece, place 1 tbsp (15 ml) flaked salmon, top with 1 or 2 prawns, then approximately 2 tbsp (30 ml) alfalfa sprouts, dollop of yogurt, and 1 or 2 coriander leaves (if using). Roll into cylinder shape. Makes 5 servings of 3 rolls each.

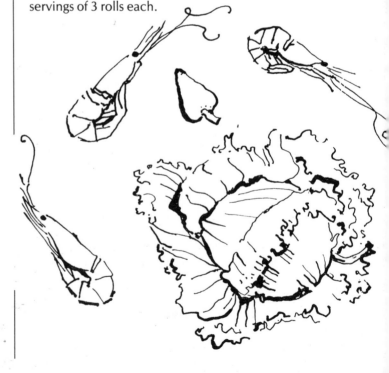

Right:
Prawn Mousse with Dill (page 19)

Marinated Mushrooms and Artichokes
Drain one can (14 oz [398 ml]) artichokes. Cut in half and add to mushroom mixture before marinating.

PER SERVING	
calories	39
g fat	2
g protein	2
g carbohydrate	5
Good: niacin, fibre	

Marinated Mushrooms

Pass these spicy mushrooms with drinks or serve as part of a relish tray or salad plate.

5 fl oz	tarragon vinegar	150 ml
5 tbsp	vegetable oil	75 ml
2 tbsp	granulated sugar	30 ml
1 tsp	each dried basil and thyme	5 ml
$\frac{1}{2}$ tsp	salt	2 ml
2 tbsp	water	30 ml
Dash	hot pepper sauce	Dash
$\frac{1}{4}$ tsp	dried hot pepper flakes (optional)	1 ml
1	clove garlic, chopped	1
	freshly ground pepper	
1	onion, sliced	1
$1\frac{1}{2}$ lb	medium mushrooms	650 g

   In large bowl, combine vinegar, oil, sugar, basil, thyme, salt, water, hot pepper sauce, dried hot pepper flakes if using, garlic, and pepper to taste; stir until well mixed.
   Separate onion into rings. Wash mushrooms and trim bases. Add onions and mushrooms to vinegar mixture; mix lightly. Cover and refrigerate for at least 8 hours, stirring occasionally. Drain before serving. Makes 10.

Mushroom-Stuffed Courgettes
For a light, refreshing, hot hors d'oeuvre follow recipe on page 125 using very thin courgettes cut into bite-size pieces. Serve on platter along with Spiced Meatballs with Coriander Dip (page 23) and cherry tomatoes.

Left:
Chunky Vegetable and Bean Soup (page 35)

Marinated Spiced Carrots

These are a favourite and can be served along with the Marinated Mushrooms (see previous page). A few cherry tomatoes on the platter look nice and add extra colour.

	PER SERVING	
calories		27
g fat		0
g protein		0.5
g carbohydrate		6
Excellent: vitamin A		

1 lb	small carrots, scraped	450 g
5 oz	granulated sugar	120 g
4 fl oz	white vinegar	125 ml
4 fl oz	water	125 ml
1 tbsp	mustard seeds	15 ml
3	whole cloves	3
1	3 in (8 cm) stick cinnamon, broken	1

Cut carrots into 3-inch-long (8 cm), very thin sticks. Blanch in boiling water for 3 minutes; drain and cool under cold water. Drain again and place in bowl.

In saucepan, combine sugar, vinegar, water, mustard seeds, cloves and cinnamon; bring to boil. Reduce heat and simmer for 10 minutes; pour over carrots. Let cool, then cover and refrigerate for at least 8 hours or overnight. Drain well; discard cloves and cinnamon. Makes approximately 10.

Warm Vegetable Salad with Tomato and Onion Dressing

Warm vegetables over cool greens is a very pleasing combination. You can prepare the vegetables and dressing in advance, then just before serving quickly blanch vegetables and add dressing. It's a lovely dinner-party first course or a light lunch.

	PER SERVING	
calories		100
g fat		8
g protein		3
g carbohydrate		7
Excellent: vitamin A, vitamin C, fibre		

½ lb	spinach	225 g
1	small Belgian endive	1
5 oz	green beans, cut 2 in (5 cm) long and sliced lengthwise	125 g
4 oz	julienne carrots	100 g
4 oz	small cauliflower florets	100 g
4 oz	small broccoli florets	100 g
3 tbsp	sunflower seeds	45 ml

Tomato and Onion Dressing

3 tbsp	vegetable oil	45 ml
3 tbsp	water	45 ml
3 tbsp	lemon juice	45 ml
2	spring onions, finely chopped	2
1 tbsp	chopped fresh basil (or ½ tsp [2 ml] dried)	15 ml
¼ tsp	Dijon mustard	2 ml
	salt and freshly ground pepper	
3	medium tomatoes, peeled and diced	3

Trim, wash and dry spinach; tear into large pieces. Separate endive leaves. On 6 salad plates, arrange spinach and endive leaves.

Tomato and Onion Dressing: In food processor or mixing bowl, combine oil, water, lemon juice, onions, basil and mustard; mix well. Season with salt and pepper to taste.

Five minutes before serving: In large pot of boiling salted water, blanch green beans, carrots, cauliflower and broccoli for 2 minutes; drain. Spoon warm vegetables onto greens; stir

Leftover Chicken or Turkey

Christmas turkey or Sunday lunch chicken leftovers can be used for a lovely lunch or dinner in the following recipes:
Curried Chicken Croustades (page 28)
Turkey Noodle Soup (page 32)
Tarragon Chicken Salad (page 46)
Curried Chicken Crêpes (page 83)
Chicken and Prawn Creole (page 87)
Old-Fashioned Chicken Pot Pie (page 83)
Pizza topping

PER CROUSTADE	
calories	30
g fat	1
g protein	3
g carbohydrate	3

Use leftover bread trimmings to make bread crumbs. Use in Herb-Breaded Chicken (page 189) or Herb-Breaded Fish Fillets (page 94).

tomatoes into dressing and spoon dressing over vegetables. Sprinkle with sunflower seeds. Serve immediately before vegetables cool. Makes 8 servings.

Curried Chicken Croustades

Serve these savoury titbits at a cocktail party or make larger croustades and serve for a luncheon dish. In this recipe tiny shells of bread are toasted and filled with curried chicken. Both parts can be made in advance, then reheated before serving. The croustades are perfect low-calorie, low-fat containers for savoury fillings.

40	thin slices bread, preferably wholemeal (about 2 loaves)	40
	Curried Chicken filling for crêpes (page 83)	

Using 2-inch (5 cm) biscuit cutter or glass, cut out 40 rounds o bread. Press bread rounds into very small tart tins (about 1½ inch [4 cm] in diameter). Bake in 300°F (150°C) Gas Mark 2 oven for 20 minutes or until toasted. Remove from oven and let cool. (Croustades can be prepared in advance and stored in covered container for up to 1 week or frozen for up to 2 months.)
Fill croustades with Curried Chicken mixture and place on baking sheet. Heat in 400°F (200°C) Gas Mark 6 oven for 15 minutes or until hot. Makes 40.

Quick, Low-Calorie, Low-Fat Hors d'Oeuvres

Cucumber Canapes

Use round cucumber slices as the base for canapes. If you wish, scoop out a tiny portion of cucumber from centre to form a hollow; top with a spoonful of:

- *Prawn Mousse with Dill (page 19);*

- *Salmon Spread with Capers (page 16);*

- *Classic Tuna Salad with Fresh Dill (page 49);*

- *or Curried Chicken (page 83).*

Mini-Pittas

Cut small (1½-inch [4 cm]) pitta bread rounds in half so that you have 2 pockets. Line pocket with a soft leaf lettuce and fill with any of the fillings listed above with Cucumber Canapes.

Fill hollowed-out cherry tomatoes, courgette rounds, mange tout or mushroom caps with any of the above spreads, or with the dip recipes in this book.

Use Belgian endive spears instead of crackers or crisps for dipping.

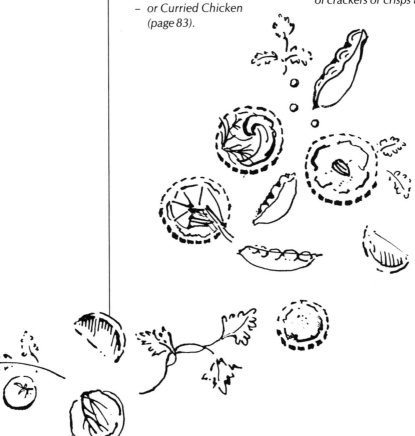

SOUPS

Homemade soup is such a treat and so easy to make that I wish always had some on hand. In this section there are elegant soups to serve as first courses at a dinner party — such as Cream of Parsnip Soup with Ginger or Fresh Beetroot and Yogurt Soup — or there's a Hearty Vegetable Bean Soup, which is a wonderfully warming main-course dish. Main-course soups are easy to prepare, make good use of leftovers and can be made ahead of time.

Canned and Packaged Soups

Canned and packaged soups are very high in salt. If you use only canned or packaged soups, your family will acquire a taste for this kind of soup. To increase the nutrients and decrease the sodium of packaged or canned soup you can use them as a base, and add more vegetables, such as grated carrot, grated courgette, chopped green beans, broccoli, cubed potatoes and/or chopped onion.

Whenever possible, add skimmed or semi-skimmed milk instead of water to canned soups; this way you increase the soup's protein and calcium content.

I often add leftover cooked rice or noodles, chicken or meats, an extra mushroom or green onion to soups.

Compare Homemade and Canned Soups

per 8 fl oz (250 ml)	g fat	mg sodium
Asparagus and Potato Bisque (page 31)	1	52
Canned cream of asparagus (with water added)	3	996
Mushroom Soup with Tarragon (page 36)	5	257
Canned cream of mushroom (with water added)	9	1091

To get the maximum flavour with the least amount of fat
When making a vegetable soup, if you cook the vegetables first in a lump of margarine, the margarine becomes absorbed into the vegetables. Instead cook vegetables in only 1 tsp (5 ml) margarine and some chicken stock, or better still in only chicken stock. To add richness of flavour add 2 tbsp (30 ml) cream or milk (single cream will add 8 g fat; whipping cream 20 g fat) just before serving. You will achieve the same effect with much less fat. (The same principle applies to salt; add it at the end of cooking or just before serving.)

Asparagus and Potato Bisque

Potato helps to thicken this soup without adding the extra calories or preparation time of a butter/flour-thickened soup. It is delicious served hot or cold, but when serving hot, substitute either single cream or milk for the yogurt, since yogurt tends to curdle easily when heated. (Recipe pictured opposite page 56.)

1	large potato, peeled and diced	1
1	small onion, chopped	1
12 fl oz	water or chicken stock	375 ml
1 lb	fresh asparagus	500 g
2 tsp	lemon juice	10 ml
8 fl oz	skimmed milk	250 ml
5 oz	low-fat natural yogurt, or single cream	120 g
	salt and freshly ground pepper	
Pinch	nutmeg	Pinch

In saucepan, combine potato, onion, and water or chicken stock; cover and simmer until potato is nearly tender, 5 to 10 minutes.

Meanwhile, cut asparagus into about 1½-inch (4 cm) lengths. Add to potato mixture; cover and simmer for 5 minutes or until asparagus is tender.

Using slotted spoon, remove asparagus tips and let cool in cold water to prevent further cooking. Drain and reserve for garnish.

In food processor or blender, purée asparagus-potato mixture; add lemon juice. Pour into bowl; cover and refrigerate until chilled. Stir in milk and yogurt; season with salt, pepper and nutmeg to taste. Serve cold or reheat. Garnish each serving with reserved asparagus tips. Makes 6 servings.

PER SERVING (made with yogurt and unsalted chicken stock)	
calories	103
g fat	1
g protein	5
g carbohydrate	19
Good: fibre, niacin	
Excellent: vitamin C	

*Instead of using salt to add flavour to soups, use onion or celery, herbs (thyme, rosemary, oregano, chives, parsley, to name just a few), lemon juice, a pinch of sugar, pepper, nutmeg or garlic. Also use more of the vegetable itself (i.e., if you are making carrot soup, add extra carrots).

PER SERVING	
calories	91
g fat	3
g protein	11
g carbohydrate	5
Good: vitamin C	
Excellent: vitamin A, niacin	

Turkey Noodle Soup

Whenever you roast a turkey or chicken, make this heart-warming soup from the leftovers. Don't be put off by the long list of ingredients; it's really quite easy to prepare. I usually start the stock simmering while I'm making dinner one night, let it simmer for a few hours that evening then finish it the next night. If you prefer, add rice instead of noodles.

Stock*

1	carcass from roast chicken or turkey**	1
3 pt	water	1.75 li
1	bay leaf	1
1	stick celery, chopped	1
1	onion, quartered	1

Soup

1 oz	broken noodles ($\frac{1}{2}$ in [1 cm] pieces)	25 g
1	stick celery (including leaves), chopped	1
1	carrot, chopped	1
3	spring onions, sliced	3
1	small courgette, grated	1
1 tsp	dried basil	5 m
1 tsp	dried thyme	5 m
Dash	hot pepper sauce	Dash
	salt and freshly ground pepper	

**If you don't have a leftover turkey or chicken carcass, use 3 pt (1.7 lit) chicken stock instead of the stock here. For a main course soup and to increase fibre add 1 can (19 oz [540 ml]) chickpeas or kidney beans, drained. Other additions: green peas, chopped fresh spinach, asparagus, chopped broccoli, diced potato, or turnip.

Stock: In stockpot or large saucepan, combine carcass, water, bay leaf, celery and onion. Simmer, covered, for 4 hours. Strain reserving stock. Let bones cool, then pick out any meat and add to stock.

Soup: In stockpot or saucepan, bring stock to boil; add noodles and simmer for 5 minutes. Add celery, carrot, green onions, courgette, basil and thyme; simmer for 10 minutes. Stir in hot pepper sauce; season with salt and pepper to taste. Make 6 servings.

Seafood Chowder

PER SERVING	
calories	185
g fat	3
g protein	21
g carbohydrate	19
Good: fibre, niacin, iron	
Excellent: vitamin A, vitamin C	

Soup Tips
*The most effective way to reduce fat in soups is to cut down the amount of butter, margarine or oil you put in them. Many recipes call for more of these than is necessary. Another way is to substitute single cream or milk for whipping cream. If you do need more fat for flavour, add it at the end of cooking — just before serving. This will give the maximum flavour for the least amount of fat.
*Traditional high-fat soup thickeners are whole milk, cream, egg yolks and high-fat cheese. Instead, thicken soups with rice, noodles, potato legumes, puréed vegetables, low-fat cheese, skimmed milk and low-fat natural yogurt.

Serve this wonderfully warming seafood stew for lunch, dinner or as late-night party fare. If fresh mussels and clams aren't available, use canned or bottled ones. Prawns can also be added. Some fish markets sell fresh fish pieces. These are usually inexpensive and ideal for this recipe; remove any skin or bones.

2 tsp	vegetable oil	10 ml
1	onion, chopped	1
1	stick celery, chopped	1
1	carrot, chopped	1
2	cloves garlic, crushed	2
1	bay leaf	1
1 tsp	dried thyme	5 ml
1 tsp	dried basil	5 ml
1	can (19 oz [540 g]) tomatoes	1
18 fl oz	water	540 ml
2	potatoes, diced	2
1 lb	mussels	450 g
1 lb	small clams (or one 5 oz [142 g] can)	450 g
1 lb	fresh white flesh fish (cod, haddock, monkfish)	450 g
4 fl oz	white wine	125 ml
	salt and freshly ground pepper	
1 oz	chopped fresh parsley	25 g

In large saucepan, heat oil over medium heat; cook onion, celery and carrot, stirring, for 5 minutes. Add garlic, bay leaf, thyme, basil, tomatoes, water and potatoes; bring to simmer. Cover and cook over low heat for 25 minutes or until vegetables are tender. Remove bay leaf.

Meanwhile, scrub mussels and clams under cold running water; cut off any hairy beards from mussels. Discard any clams

Quick Gazpacho
Don't throw away leftover tossed green salads made with an oil-and-vinegar dressing. Instead, purée in a blender or food processor and add tomato juice to taste. Refrigerate until cold then serve in soup bowls, topped with finely chopped tomato, green pepper and garlic croutons.

PER SERVING	
calories	85
g fat	4
g protein	6
g carbohydrate	7
Good: vitamin C, calcium	

or mussels that do not close when tapped. Add clams to saucepan; simmer for 5 minutes. Add mussels, fish (if using monkfish cut into chunks) and wine. Simmer for 5 minutes or until clams and mussels open; discard any that don't open. Season with salt and pepper to taste. Just before serving sprinkle with parsley. (Chowder can be prepared up to 1 day in advance, refrigerated and reheated.) Makes 6 servings.

Chilled Cucumber and Chive Soup

Quick to prepare, this wonderful summer soup is perfect for lunch or picnic or a first course for an alfresco dinner. For packed lunches it's easy to transport in a Thermos flask .

5 oz	cottage cheese	125 g
5 oz	sour cream	125 g
16 fl oz	buttermilk	500 ml
$\frac{1}{2}$	unpeeled cucumber, diced	$\frac{1}{2}$
1 oz	chopped fresh parsley	25 g
1 oz	diced red radishes	25 g
$1\frac{1}{2}$ oz	chopped fresh chives or spring onions	35 g
	salt and freshly ground pepper	

   In blender or food processor, process cottage cheese and sour cream until smooth; add buttermilk and process to mix.
   Transfer to bowl; stir in cucumber, parsley, radishes and chives. Season with salt and pepper to taste. Refrigerate until chilled. Makes 6 servings.

PER SERVING	
calories	151
g fat	2
g protein	9
g carbohydrate	25
Good: vitamin C, iron	
Excellent: fibre, vitamin A, niacin	

Chunky Vegetable and Bean Soup

Onion and potato are the basis for this soup — the potato helps to thicken it, the onions add flavour. You can add any seasonal fresh vegetables — broccoli, mushrooms, courgettes, carrots, tomatoes — that you have on hand. Instead of canned kidney beans, you can add 1 oz (30 g) uncooked noodles, or rice or barley, along with the potato. (Recipe pictured opposite page 25.)

1	large onion, chopped	1
1	large potato, peeled and cubed	1
1¾ pt	chicken stock	1 lit
2	sticks celery, diced	2
4 oz	green beans, cut in 1 in (2.5 cm) pieces	100 g
¼	small cabbage, thinly sliced, and/or ½ pkg spinach, coarsely sliced	¼
1	carrot, grated or chopped	1
1½ oz	chopped sweet red pepper	40 g
1 tsp	dried dillweed (or 1 oz [25 g] chopped fresh)	5 ml
1	can (19 oz [540 g]) kidney beans, drained	1
	salt, cayenne and freshly ground pepper	
2 oz	grated Parmesan cheese (optional)	50 g

In large heavy saucepan, combine onion, potato and chicken stock; bring to a boil. Reduce heat and simmer for 10 minutes.

Add celery, green beans, cabbage and/or spinach, carrot, red pepper, dillweed and kidney beans; cover and simmer for 10 minutes or until vegetables are tender.

Season with salt, cayenne and pepper to taste. Sprinkle each serving with Parmesan (if using). Makes 8 servings.

Mushroom Soup with Tarragon

Easy to make, this creamy soup tastes so much better than anything out of a can.

PER SERVING	
calories	107
g fat	5
g protein	6
g carbohydrate	10
Good: vitamin C, niacin	

½ lb	mushrooms	225 g
1 tbsp	unsaturated margarine	15 ml
2 tbsp	onion, finely chopped	30 ml
2 tbsp	plain flour	30 ml
8 fl oz	hot chicken stock	250 ml
12 fl oz	skimmed milk	375 ml
1 tsp	dried tarragon	5 ml
½ oz	chopped fresh parsley	12 g
	salt and freshly ground pepper	

Thinly slice 4 mushroom caps and set aside; coarsely chop remaining mushrooms (if using food processor, use on-off turns).

In saucepan, melt margarine over medium heat; add onion and cook for 2 minutes, stirring occasionally. Add chopped mushrooms and cook for 4 minutes, stirring often; sprinkle with flour and stir until mixed. Whisk in hot chicken stock and bring to boil, whisking constantly. Reduce heat to low and add milk, tarragon, parsley and reserved sliced mushrooms; simmer, uncovered, for 4 minutes.

Season to taste with salt and pepper. Makes 4 servings.

Compare

per 8 fl oz (250 ml)	calories	g fat	g protein	g fibre
Canned Chunky Vegetable Soup	104	3	3	3
Canned Vegetable Soup	80	2	2	1
Homemade Chunky Vegetable and Bean Soup	151	2	9	7

Fresh Corn Bisque with Spring Onions

When corn on the cob is in season, try this fresh-tasting, economical soup. The recipe can easily be halved, or you can freeze any extra in container sizes to suit your household.

2 tbsp	vegetable oil	30 ml
1	onion, chopped	1
1	carrot, chopped	1
1	stick celery, chopped	1
2	cloves garlic, crushed	2
$\frac{1}{2}$ tsp	turmeric	2 ml
1	bay leaf	1
$1\frac{3}{4}$ pt	water	1 lit
5	corn on the cob	5
$\frac{1}{2}$ tsp	salt	2 ml
	cayenne pepper	
$\frac{1}{2}$ oz	chopped spring onions or fresh coriander	12 g

In large saucepan, heat oil over medium heat. Add onion, carrot, celery and garlic; cook, stirring, for 2 minutes. Stir in turmeric and cook for 1 minute. Add bay leaf and water; bring to simmer.

Cut corn kernels from cobs and set aside. Add cobs to saucepan; cover and simmer for 10 minutes. Add corn kernels and simmer for 10 minutes longer. Discard corn cobs and bay leaf. Reserve about 2 oz (50 g) sweet corn.

In blender or food processor, purée mixture in batches. Return to saucepan and add reserved sweet corn, salt, and cayenne to taste. Serve hot or cold and garnish with green onions or coriander. Makes 8 servings.

Cream of Parsnip Soup with Ginger

Microwave parsnips and leeks separately in large amounts then freeze them in smaller portions to be able to prepare this splendid soup at the last minute.

SERVING	
calories	111
g fat	3
g protein	3
g carbohydrate	17
Good: fibre, vitamin C	

1	onion (or 2 whites of leeks), chopped	1
4	medium parsnips, peeled and cubed (about 10 oz [280 g])	4
8 fl oz	water	250 m
1 tbsp	unsaturated margarine	15 m
2 tbsp	plain flour	30 m
8 fl oz	chicken stock	250 m
1½ tsp	grated fresh root ginger	7 m
7 fl oz	skimmed milk	225 m
	salt and white pepper	

In saucepan, combine onion, parsnips and water; simmer, covered, for 8 to 10 minutes or until parsnips are tender. Purée in blender or food processor and set aside.

In saucepan, melt margarine over medium heat; stir in flour and cook for 1 minute. Stir in chicken stock and cook, stirring, until mixture comes to boil and thickens.

Add puréed parsnip mixture, root ginger, milk, and salt and pepper to taste. Stir to mix well and heat through. Serve hot or cold. (If too thick, thin with more milk or chicken stock.) Makes 5 servings.

PER SERVING	
calories	99
g fat	4
g protein	3
g carbohydrate	13
Good: vitamin C, niacin	

Pumpkin and Courgette Soup

This is a delightful winter soup. If you don't peel the courgette, the soup will be green in colour; if peeled it will be pumpkin-coloured.

15 oz	peeled, cubed pumpkin	375 g
15 oz	cubed courgettes	375 g
2	medium potatoes, peeled and cubed	2
1	large onion, sliced	1
16 fl oz	chicken stock	500 ml
2 tbsp	vegetable oil	30 ml
2 tbsp	chopped fresh parsley	30 ml
2	cloves garlic, crushed	2
7 fl oz	skimmed milk	225 ml
1 tsp	dried basil (or 2 tbsp [30 ml] chopped fresh)	5 ml
	fresh mint leaves or chopped fresh parsley	

In large saucepan, combine pumpkin, courgettes, potatoes, onion, chicken stock, oil, parsley and garlic. Cover and simmer, stirring occasionally, for 45 minutes or until vegetables are tender. If stock simmers down, add water to reach original level.

In food processor or blender, purée mixture in batches; return to saucepan. Add milk and basil; heat until hot. Garnish each serving with mint leaves. Makes 8 servings.

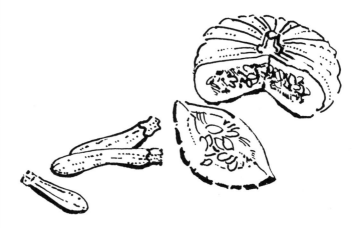

Courgette and Watercress Vichyssoise

This light, elegant, quick-to-prepare soup is perfect for the first course of a dinner party. Serve it hot in the spring when the first crop of watercress appears, or chilled in the summer for a refreshing starter.

PER SERVING	
calories	80
g fat	1
g protein	4
g carbohydrate	14
Good: vitamin C, niacin	

1 lb	courgettes (about 4 small), sliced	450 g
1	large potato, peeled and diced	
1	medium onion, chopped	
16 fl oz	chicken stock	500 m
1 tbsp	lemon juice	15 m
3 oz	watercress leaves	75 g
12 fl oz	skimmed milk	375 m
	salt and freshly ground pepper	

In saucepan, combine courgettes, potato, onion and chicken stock; cover and simmer until vegetables are tender, 15 to 20 minutes.

In food processor or blender, purée hot mixture with lemon juice and watercress until smooth. Stir in milk, salt and pepper to taste; reheat if necessary and serve hot. Alternatively, cover and refrigerate until cold. To serve, thin with additional milk if too thick and garnish with watercress leaves. Makes 8 servings.

Microwave Method
In microwave-safe dish, combine courgettes, potato and onion with 2 tbsp (30 ml) of the chicken stock. Cover and microwave at high (100% power) until vegetables are tender, 10 to 13 minutes, rotating every few minutes and stirring after 6 minutes.

In food processor or blender, purée mixture until smooth, adding some of the remaining chicken stock if too thick to process. Return to dish and stir in remaining chicken stock, lemon juice, watercress and milk. Add salt and pepper to taste and reheat or serve cold.

Beetroot and Yogurt Soup

This beautiful red soup has a wonderful fresh beet taste when made with small, tender beetroots. I once made the mistake of making it in the winter using large, old beetroots and it was nowhere near as good. (Recipe pictured opposite page 56.)

	PER SERVING	
calories		75
g fat		2
g protein		3
g carbohydrate		12
Good: fibre, vitamin C		
Excellent: vitamin A		

2 lb	small beetroots	1 kg
1 tbsp	unsaturated margarine	15 ml
1	large onion, chopped	1
2 fl oz	lemon juice	60 ml
2 tbsp	drained horseradish	30 ml
1	large carrot, grated	1
8 fl oz	chicken stock	250 ml
6 oz	low-fat natural yogurt	150 g
	salt and freshly ground pepper	

Garnish

	Yogurt and thin strips or slices lemon or orange rind	

Wash beetroots and trim, leaving 1 inch (2.5 cm) of the ends attached.

In large saucepan, cover beetroots with water and bring to boil; reduce heat and simmer, covered, for 20 to 30 minutes or until tender. Remove beetroots from saucepan; reserve cooking liquid. When beetroots are cool enough to handle (or under cold running water), slip off skins and stems. Cut beetroots in half.

In large saucepan, melt margarine over medium heat; add onion and cook until tender. Add 1¼ pt (750 ml) reserved cooking liquid, beetroots, lemon juice, horseradish, carrot and chicken stock; simmer for 5 minutes.

In blender or food processor, purée mixture in batches and return to saucepan; stir in yogurt. Season with salt and pepper to taste. Reheat over medium-low heat being careful not to boil. Garnish each serving with spoonful of yogurt and strips of orange or lemon rind. Makes 8 servings.

Fresh Tomato Soup Provençal

Fresh herbs add a delightful flavour to this soup. If the herbs in this recipe aren't available, use other fresh herbs, such as dill instead of basil and oregano instead of thyme. For a lighter soup, omit milk and add a little more chicken stock.

	PER SERVING	
calories		50
g fat		1
g protein		3
g carbohydrate		8
Good: fibre, vitamin A		
Excellent: vitamin C		

3	large tomatoes, quartered (about 1¼ lb [550 g])	3
1	medium onion, sliced	1
1	clove garlic, chopped	1
10 fl oz	chicken stock	300 ml
2 tbsp	tomato purée	30 ml
½ oz	chopped fresh parsley	12 g
½ oz	chopped fresh basil (or 1 tsp [5 ml] dried*)	12 g
1 tbsp	chopped fresh thyme (or ½ tsp [2 ml] dried)	15 ml
6 fl oz	skimmed milk	180 ml
	salt and freshly ground pepper	

Garnish

	Fresh thyme sprigs or basil leaves	

In saucepan, combine tomatoes, onion, garlic, chicken stock; cover and simmer for 15 minutes.

Transfer to blender or food processor; add tomato purée and process until smooth. Stir in parsley, basil, thyme and milk; season with salt and pepper to taste.

Cover and refrigerate to serve chilled, or reheat over medium heat and serve hot. Garnish each serving with thyme sprigs or basil leaves. Makes 6 servings.

*A general rule for substituting fresh for dried herbs is to use 3 times the amount of fresh. However, with Tomato Soup Provençal I like a lot more fresh herbs than usual. The amount will also vary depending upon how hard you pack the fresh herbs when measuring.

Split Pea, Bean and Barley Soup

When you want something that is a light yet warming meal, this soup is just right. Serve it with toast or hot French bread and a green salad.

1 tbsp	vegetable oil	15 ml
2	onions, chopped	2
4 oz	dried green split peas	100 g
2 oz	dried lima beans	50 g
2 oz	barley	50 g
2 pt	water	1.25 lit
1	bay leaf	1
1 tsp	celery seeds	5 ml
1	potato, diced	1
1	carrot, chopped	1
1	stick celery (including leaves), chopped	1
1 tsp	dried basil	5 ml
1 tsp	salt	5 ml
½ tsp	dried thyme	2 ml
	freshly ground pepper	

In large heavy saucepan, heat oil over medium heat; add onions and cook, stirring, until tender.

Rinse split peas and lima beans, discarding any shrivelled or discoloured ones. Add to saucepan along with barley, water, bay leaf and celery seeds. Bring to boil; reduce heat and simmer, covered, for 1½ hours.

Add potato, carrot, celery, basil, salt, thyme and pepper; simmer for 30 minutes or until vegetables are tender. Remove bay leaf. If too thick, add water to reach desired thickness. Makes 6 servings.

Chilled Carrot and Coriander Soup

Be sure to use tender young carrots when making this sweet, flavourful soup. Fresh coriander adds a special extra flavour; it's available at most Chinese food stores and many fruit and vegetable stores that sell fresh herbs. Coriander seeds can easily be ground in a coffee or spice grinder. (Recipe pictured opposite page 56.)

PER SERVING	
calories	58
g fat	1
g protein	4
g carbohydrate	9
Good: fibre, niacin	
Excellent: vitamin A	

1	onion, chopped	1
1 lb	young carrots, scraped and sliced	450 g
1 tsp	ground coriander	5 ml
1½ pt	chicken stock	900 ml
½ oz	chopped fresh coriander leaves or parsley	12 g
	salt and freshly ground pepper	

Garnish

	Yogurt or sour cream, sunflower seeds, coriander leaves or parsley	

In saucepan, combine onion, carrots, ground coriander and chicken stock; cover and simmer until vegetables are tender, 15 to 20 minutes.

In food processor or blender, purée mixture until smooth. Stir in fresh coriander. Add salt and pepper to taste. Serve hot, or cover and refrigerate until cold.

Garnish each serving with spoonful of yogurt or sour cream, sprinkling of sunflower seeds and chopped fresh coriander leaves or parsley. Makes 6 servings.

Microwave Method
In microwave-safe dish, combine onion, carrots, ground coriander and 2 tbsp (30 ml) chicken stock. Cover and microwave at high (100%) power for 8 to 12 minutes or until carrots are tender. (Time will vary depending on thickness of slices and age of carrots.)

In food processor or blender, purée mixture until smooth. Stir in fresh coriander and remaining chicken stock; season with salt and pepper to taste. Reheat or refrigerate until cold.

Basic Chicken Stock

PER ½ pt (300 ml) SERVING	
calories	3
g fat	0
g protein	0
g carbohydrate	0

As well as its much better flavour, the main reason for recommending homemade chicken stock is its low salt content. If you're not in the habit of making chicken stock, it can seem very time-consuming. Once you start making it you'll realize how easy it is. Any pieces of chicken can be used, even a whole chicken (giblets removed). Backs and necks are least expensive.

4 lb	chicken, whole or pieces	2 kg
5 pt	cold water	3 lit
2	carrots, chopped	2
2	onions, chopped	2
2	sticks celery, chopped	2
2	bay leaves	2
6	black peppercorns	6
2	sprigs fresh thyme (or pinch each dried thyme, basil and marjoram)	2

When Making Stock

After chicken is cooked, remove meat from bones and use in salads (see Tarragon Chicken Salad, page 46), Curried Chicken Crêpes (page 83), Curried Chicken Croustades (page 28), sandwiches or add to soups. Freeze homemade chicken stock in ice-cube trays or small containers and use in cooking whenever you want extra flavour without added salt. Use in soups, salad dressings, sauces, stir-frys.

Variations

Turkey Stock

Use turkey bones or carcass instead of chicken.

Beef, Veal or Lamb Stock

Use beef, veal or lamb bones instead of chicken. For added flavour, roast bones before simmering in water. Spread bones in roasting pan and bake in 400°F (200°C) Gas Mark 6 oven for 1 hour or until browned; transfer to stock-pot and continue as in Basic Chicken Stock recipe.

In stockpot, combine chicken and water; bring to boil. Skim off any scum. Add carrots, onions, celery, bay leaves, peppercorns and thyme; simmer, uncovered, for 4 hours.

Remove from heat and strain; cover and refrigerate stock until any fat congeals on surface. Remove fat layer. Refrigerate for up to 2 days or freeze for longer storage. Makes approximately 4 pt (2 lit).

Compare	mg sodium per 8 fl oz (250 ml)
This recipe	4
Chicken broth from cube	762

Chicken Salad Sandwich Deluxe

Spread Tarragon Chicken Salad on pumpernickel, a bagel, or toasted Italian bread. Add any combination of lettuce, watercress or sliced tomato. Serve open-faced or top with bread.

PER SERVING	
calories	170
g fat	8
g protein	21
g carbohydrate	4
Excellent: niacin	

*To toast almonds, roast on pie plate in 350°F (180°C) Gas Mark 4 oven for 5 minutes or until golden.

SALADS AND DRESSINGS

My favourite salads are so simple that they hardly qualify as recipes. I love thick slices of juicy tomatoes sprinkled with fresh basil, coarsely ground pepper and a tiny drizzle of olive oil. Another favourite is fresh, tender spinach leaves, sliced mushroom and balsamic vinegar, or Oakleaf lettuce and Walnut Oil Vinaigrette.

Salad dressings are easy to make. Homemade dressings taste much better, and are less expensive and often healthier than shop-bought. Commercial salad dressings tend to be high in calories and salt, and are generally made of poorer-quality fats and oils.

For salad dressings I usually use safflower oil or olive oil or a combination of both. For a special green salad I love to add some walnut oil. See page 209 for more information on oils.

Tarragon Chicken Salad

This light and easy-to-make salad is lovely for a special lunch or dinner on a hot summer day. Serve on lettuce or with a green salad and chilled cooked asparagus or sliced tomatoes. Cook chicken in microwave or simmer in water and use liquid for stock (see Basic Chicken Stock recipe page 45).

1 lb	cooked cubed chicken	450 g
6 oz	sliced celery	150 g
½ oz	chopped chives or spring onions	12 g
5 oz	low-fat natural yogurt	125 g
2½ oz	sour cream or low-fat mayonnaise	60 g
1½ tsp	dried tarragon	7 ml
2 tbsp	toasted* slivered almonds	30 ml
	salt and freshly ground pepper	

In large bowl, combine chicken, celery, chives or onions, yogurt, sour cream or mayonnaise and tarragon; mix lightly. Cover and refrigerate for 1 hour or up to 24 hours. Just before serving, add almonds; season with salt and pepper to taste. Makes 6 servings.

PER SERVING	
calories	107
g fat	4
g protein	5
g carbohydrate	15
Good: vitamin C, iron	
Excellent: fibre	

Red kidney beans or chickpeas can be used instead of white kidney beans. All are an excellent source of fibre.

Remember this salad when you are making packed lunches. It will be a welcome change from sandwiches.

White Bean, Radish and Red Onion Salad

This looks attractive on red leaf lettuce. It goes well on a summer salad plate, a buffet dinner, or with barbecued hamburgers and lamb chops.

1	can (19 oz [540 g]) white beans, e.g. Cannellini, drained	1
3 oz	red onion, chopped	75 g
6 oz	thinly sliced or diced cucumber	150 g
4 oz	sliced radishes	100 g
1	clove garlic, crushed	1
1 oz	chopped fresh parsley	25 g
3 tbsp	lemon juice or sherry vinegar	45 ml
2 tbsp	vegetable oil	30 ml
	salt and freshly ground pepper	
	red leaf lettuce	

In sieve or colander, rinse beans under cold water; drain and place in salad bowl. Add onion, cucumber, radishes, garlic and parsley; toss to mix. Add lemon juice and oil, salt and pepper to taste; toss. Salad can be prepared to this point, covered and refrigerated for up to 2 days.

At serving time, arrange salad on bed of red lettuce. Makes 8 servings.

Compare	Per Serving	
Tarragon Chicken Salad made with:	g fat	calories
Yogurt, 5 oz (125 g) plus sour cream, 2½ oz (60 g)	8	170
Sour cream, 7½ oz (190 g)	10	186
Mayonnaise, 7½ oz (190 g)	27	331

Mange Tout and Red Pepper Buffet Salad

This colourful dish is perfect for buffet meals any time of the year. The salad can be prepared in advance; however to keep the mange tout's bright green colour, add the dressing just before serving. To make a larger amount, double salad ingredients but use same amount of dressing. (Recipe pictured opposite page 57.)

	PER SERVING	
	calories	80
	g fat	5
	g protein	3
	g carbohydrate	8
	Good: fibre, niacin	
	Excellent: vitamin C	

¾ lb	mange tout	300 g
2 tbsp	sesame seeds	30 m
½ lb	mushrooms, sliced	225 g
1	small sweet red pepper, cut in thin strips	1

Walnut Orange Dressing

1	clove garlic, crushed	1
4 fl oz	orange juice	125 m
3 tbsp	cider or white wine vinegar	45 m
1 tsp	granulated sugar	5 m
	salt	
2 tbsp	vegetable or walnut oil	30 m
	freshly ground pepper	

Nut oils
Nut oils, such as walnut oil, add a delicious flavour to salads. Use with tossed green salads or as suggested in the Mange Tout and Red Pepper Buffet Salad. Store walnut oil in refrigerator and use within a few months, as it can become rancid.

Top and string mange tout; blanch in boiling water for 2 minutes or until bright green and slightly pliable. Drain and rinse under cold water; dry thoroughly and set aside.

In ungreased pan over medium heat, cook sesame seeds, shaking pan often, for 2 minutes or until lightly browned. Set aside.

Dressing: In food processor or bowl, combine garlic, orange juice, vinegar, sugar and salt. With machine running or while mixing, gradually add oil.

In salad bowl, combine mange tout, mushrooms and red pepper. Just before serving, add dressing and sesame seeds; toss to mix. Makes 8 servings.

Classic Tuna Salad with Fresh Dill

Use this easy-to-make tuna dish as part of a summer salad — served, perhaps, in a hollowed-out tomato or papaya half — for sandwich fillings, or as an hors d'oeuvre when stuffed in cherry tomatoes, mushrooms or hollowed-out cucumber rounds.

1	can (6.5 oz [184 g]) tuna, packed in water	1
1 oz	diced celery	25 g
$\frac{1}{2}$ oz	chopped fresh dill	12 g
2 tbsp	chopped fresh parsley	30 ml
2 tbsp	chopped chives or spring onions	30 ml
2 tbsp	low-fat mayonnaise	30 ml
2 tbsp	low-fat natural yogurt	30 ml
$\frac{1}{2}$ tsp	Dijon mustard	2 ml

In bowl, mash tuna with juices.* Add celery, dill, parsley, chives, mayonnaise, yogurt and mustard; mix well. Makes 5 servings.

Alfresco Summer Supper

per serving	g fat	calories
Chilled Cucumber and Chive Soup (page 34)	4	85
Pasta and Fresh Vegetable Salad (page 59)	6	165
Sliced cold chicken breast (no skin) (4 oz [100 g])	4	187
Wholemeal rolls	2	156
(1 tsp [5 ml]) unsaturated margarine	4	33
Sliced peaches and blackberries	0	90
Skimmed milk ($\frac{1}{2}$ pt [300 ml])	0	90
Totals	20	806
Calories from fat = 22%		

PER SERVING	
calories	86
g fat	5
g protein	10
g carbohydrate	1
Excellent: niacin	

*If you only have tuna packed in oil, drain thoroughly and add more yogurt to taste.

Tuna Fish
When buying canned tuna fish, choose tuna packed in water rather than tuna packed in oil because it is lower in fat. Both kinds have the same amount of omega 3 fatty acids from fish oils. (The oil tuna is packed in is not usually from fish oils.) Always drain all fluid off.

Hidden Fat in Salad Dressings
The fat content in salads comes mainly from the oil in the dressing and can be very deceptive. The amount of oil in the Tomato, Broccoli and Pasta Salad (page 108) is at least half the amount that you would find in most salad recipes of this type. And, even with a reduced amount of oil and a small amount of low-fat cheese the fat content is higher than some of the meat, chicken and fish recipes in this book. A tossed green salad with 2 tbsp (30 ml) of a standard oil-and-vinegar dressing per serving has 20 g of fat. This is $\frac{1}{4}$ of the fat most women require in a day.

SERVING	
calories	33
g fat	2
g protein	1
g carbohydrate	4

Sliced Cucumbers with Chives, Yogurt and Basil

Serve this cooling salad with curries, paella, seafood or as part of a buffet any time of year. If chives aren't available, substitute spring onions, and fresh chopped dill can be used instead of basil.

1	cucumber	1
$\frac{1}{4}$ tsp	salt	1 ml
$2\frac{1}{2}$ oz	sour cream or fromage frais	60 g
$2\frac{1}{2}$ oz	low-fat natural yogurt	60 g
2 tbsp	chopped chives	30 ml
2 tsp	lemon juice	10 ml
1 tbsp	chopped fresh basil (or $\frac{1}{4}$ tsp [1 ml] dried)	15 ml
$\frac{1}{4}$ tsp	granulated sugar	1 ml
	freshly ground pepper	

   Peel cucumbers only if skin is tough or waxy. In food processor or by hand, thinly slice cucumbers. Place in colander and sprinkle with salt. Toss then let stand for 30 to 40 minutes. Rinse under cold water, then pat dry.
   In bowl, combine sour cream, yogurt, chives, lemon juice, basil and sugar; mix well. Stir in cucumber; season with pepper to taste.
   Serve in shallow bowl or on plate. Makes 6 servings.

Curried Rice Salad

Prepare Italian Rice Salad but substitute 1 tsp (5 ml) each curry powder and cumin for thyme, basil and oregano. Add more curry to taste.

PER SERVING	
calories	187
g fat	7
g protein	5
g carbohydrate	25
Good: vitamin A, vitamin C, niacin	

Italian Rice and Mozzarella Salad

This is a handy salad to have for quick summer meals and is a great way to use up leftover cooked rice; use brown rice if you have it. It's not necessary to follow this recipe exactly; rather, use it as a guide and add whatever vegetables or cooked meats you have available. Chopped courgettes, cauliflower or artichokes are nice additions. (Recipe pictured opposite page 57.)

$1\frac{1}{2}$ lb	cooked rice	665 g
1 oz	diced carrots	25 g
1 oz	diced celery	25 g
1 oz	diced red or green pepper	25 g
3 oz	frozen peas	75 g
1 oz	chopped red onion	25 g
$\frac{1}{2}$ oz	chopped fresh parsley	12 g
$1\frac{1}{2}$ oz	diced low-fat cheese (e.g., mozzarella)	40 g
3 tbsp	cider vinegar	45 ml
2 tbsp	olive or vegetable oil	30 ml
2 tbsp	orange juice	30 ml
1 tbsp	low-calorie mayonnaise	15 ml
$\frac{1}{4}$ tsp	dried thyme (or 1 tsp [5 ml] fresh)	1 ml
$\frac{1}{4}$ tsp	dried oregano (or 1 tsp [5 ml] fresh)	1 ml
	freshly ground pepper	

In salad bowl, combine rice, carrots, celery, red pepper, peas, onion, parsley and cheese; set aside. In small bowl, combine vinegar, oil, orange juice, mayonnaise, thyme, basil and oregano; mix well. Pour over salad and toss to mix. Season with pepper to taste. Makes approximately 6 servings.

PER SERVING	
calories	30
g fat	2
g protein	1
g carbohydrate	3
Good: vitamin C	

Seasonal Salad Additions
Winter
Cherry tomatoes, sections of orange or grapefruit, sliced green apples, bean sprouts, sunflower seeds
Spring
Blanched asparagus, chives, watercress
Summer
Radish, cucumber, tomato, spring onions, fresh basil — parsley, rose or geranium petals
Autumn
Red, green or yellow peppers, cauliflower, broccoli, radicchio
Nutrition Note
The darker the green in lettuce, the higher the vitamins A and C content. Choose spinach more often than lettuce for salads; it is higher in nutrients, particularly vitamins A and C, iron and fibre.

Tossed Seasonal Greens

The best green salads are made up of an interesting and colourful variety of lettuces combined with a delicious dressing. Choose whatever lettuces are freshest in the market — leaf lettuce, mâche, endive, radicchio, or spinach and Belgian endive. Add watercress or a seasonal fruit or vegetable, such as the suggestions on the side of this page.

1	small head red leaf lettuce	1
1	small romaine lettuce	1
1	red onion, thinly sliced	1

Herb Vinaigrette

1	clove garlic, crushed	1
2 tbsp	tarragon or white wine vinegar	30 m
1 tsp	Dijon mustard	5 m
1 tbsp	olive or walnut oil	15 m
2½ fl oz	water, orange juice, unsweetened pineapple juice or chicken stock	75 m
1	spring onion, minced	1
½ oz	chopped fresh parsley	12 g

Wash lettuce leaves; spin dry or dry in paper or tea towels. Wrap in paper towels and refrigerate until needed.

Herb Vinaigrette: In food processor, blender or bowl, combine garlic, vinegar, mustard, oil and water; mix well. Stir in onion and parsley.

Just before serving, tear lettuce into pieces and place in salad bowl. Separate red onion into rings; add to bowl. (Add any other seasonal salad ingredients if using.) Drizzle with dressing and toss to mix. Makes 8 servings.

Compare: One way to reduce the fat in a salad dressing is to substitute another liquid for part of the oil. For example, in the Tossed Seasonal Greens with Herb Vinaigrette there is only 1 tbsp (15 ml) oil and 2 fl oz (60 ml) water or stock or fruit juice.

per serving	g fat	calories
This recipe	2	30
Seasonal greens using dressing made with 3 fl oz (90 ml) oil	9	93

Spinach Salad with Sesame Seed Dressing

Bright red strawberries are beautiful in this entertaining salad. In winter, use mandarin oranges, grapefruit sections or sliced green apple instead of strawberries.

1 lb	spinach	450 g
2 oz	sliced almonds	50 g
$\frac{1}{2}$ lb	firm strawberries, sliced	225 g
Sesame Seed Dressing		
1 tbsp	sesame seeds	15 ml
3 tbsp	cider vinegar	45 ml
3 tbsp	vegetable or walnut oil	45 ml
3 tbsp	water	45 ml
1 tbsp	granulated sugar	15 ml
1 tsp	poppy seeds	5 ml
$\frac{1}{4}$ tsp	paprika	1 ml
$\frac{1}{4}$ tsp	Worcestershire Sauce	1 ml
1	spring onion, minced	1

Trim, wash and dry spinach; tear into bite-size pieces. Place in salad bowl and set aside.

Sprinkle almonds on baking sheet and roast in 350°F (180°C) Gas Mark 4 oven for 5 minutes or until golden brown; set aside.

Sesame Seed Dressing: Place sesame seeds in ungreased pan, stir over medium-high heat until lightly browned. In bowl or jar, combine sesame seeds, vinegar, oil, water, sugar, poppy seeds, paprika, Worcestershire Sauce and spring onion; mix well.

Just before serving, pour dressing over spinach and toss well to coat. Add strawberries and almonds; toss lightly. Makes 10 servings.

PER SERVING	
calories	93
g fat	7
g protein	3
g carbohydrate	6

Good: fibre, iron
Excellent: vitamin A, vitamin C

For a Main-Course Salad
Add slices of chicken, either
Classic Tuna Salad with Fresh
Dill (page 49), or strips of low-
fat cheese. To complete it,
choose from what you have on
hand — such as florets of
broccoli or cauliflower.

**To Cook Bulgur or Cracked
Wheat**
In saucepan combine with
twice as much water and
simmer for 15 to 20 minutes or
until tender but not mushy.
    To serve as a vegetable add
seasonings such as salt,
pepper, lemon juice, herbs or
vegetables.
    To use in salads drain well,
cool and combine with
dressing and chopped
vegetables.
    To use in stuffings combine
with onion and herbs, such as
sage and thyme.

Carrot and Cracked-Wheat Salad with Yogurt and Herb Dressing

Bulgur or cracked wheat, available at some supermarkets and
most health food stores, is a nutty-tasting grain that is delicious
in salads or as a vegetable. It's a good source of fibre. Save any
leftover dressing and use as a dip with vegetables or as a sauce
with fish. (Recipe pictured opposite page 57.)

3 oz	bulgur or cracked wheat	75
3 oz	chopped spring onions	75
2 oz	chopped celery	50
2 oz	grated carrot	50
	salt and freshly ground pepper	
½	lettuce	

Garnish

	Sliced tomatoes, cucumber, mushrooms and radishes, chopped fresh parsley	

Yogurt and Herb Dressing

4 oz	low-fat natural yogurt	100
4 oz	sour cream	100
1 tsp	Dijon mustard	5 m
1 tsp	each dried oregano and basil (or 2 tbsp [30 ml] chopped fresh)	5 m
	salt and freshly ground pepper	

In bowl, cover bulgur with very hot water. Let stand for 1
hour; drain well. Add spring onions, celery, and carrot.
    Yogurt and Herb Dressing: Combine yogurt, sour cream,
mustard, oregano, basil, salt and pepper to taste; mix well. Pour
just enough dressing over bulgur mixture to moisten, reserving
remaining dressing; toss to mix. Cover and refrigerate for at least
1 hour or up to 2 days.
    Just before serving, toss salad again; add salt and pepper to
taste. On large platter, arrange lettuce leaves. Mound bulgur
salad in centre.
    Garnish: Surround salad with slices of tomato, cucumber,
mushrooms and radishes; sprinkle with parsley. Pass extra
dressing separately. Makes 4 large servings.

PER SERVING	
calories	152
g fat	5
g protein	6
g carbohydrate	22
Good: fibre, vitamin C	
Excellent: vitamin A	

Danish Potato Salad with Dill

Dijon mustard and fresh dill add extra flavour to this summer salad. If fresh dill isn't available, use 1 tsp (5 ml) dried dillweed and 2 oz (50 g) chopped fresh parsley.

2 lb	potatoes	1 kg
9 oz	low-fat natural yogurt	230 g
3 tbsp	low-calorie mayonnaise	45 ml
1½ oz	spring onion, finely chopped	40 g
1 tsp	curry powder	5 ml
1 tsp	Dijon mustard	5 ml
½ tsp	salt	2 ml
½ oz	chopped fresh dill	12 g
	freshly ground pepper	

Garnish

	Watercress (optional)	

Wash potatoes and cook in large pot of boiling water until tender. Drain and let cool slightly; peel only if skins are tough and cut into thin slices.

In bowl, mix together yogurt, mayonnaise, onion, curry powder, mustard and salt. Add potatoes, dill, and pepper to taste; stir gently. Garnish each serving with watercress (if using). Makes 6 servings.

PER SERVING

calories	169
g fat	4
g protein	5
g carbohydrate	31

Good: fibre, niacin
Excellent: vitamin C

Potatoes, including skin, are a good source of fibre. Without the skin the amount of fibre is reduced by half.

Compare	per 2 oz (50 g) serving	
	g fat	calories
Salad made with:		
Low-fat natural yogurt (plus 3 tbsp [45 ml] low-calorie mayonnaise)	4	169
Low-calorie mayonnaise	16	269
Mayonnaise	33	420

Curried Vermicelli Noodle Salad

This salad is easy to prepare, especially in large quantities, and is perfect for buffets or hot-weather dining.

PER SERVING	
calories	200
g fat	10
g protein	6
g carbohydrate	25
Good: fibre, vitamin C, niacin, iron	

½ lb	vermicelli noodles*	225
2 oz	pine nuts	50
1 oz	coarsely chopped fresh parsley	25
Curry Dressing		
4 oz	pearl onions	100
2½ fl oz	olive oil	75 m
2 tsp	curry powder	10 m
1½ tsp	ground coriander	7 m
½ tsp	ground cardamom	2 m
¼ tsp	turmeric	1 m
½ tsp	garlic, crushed	2 m
12 fl oz	beef or chicken stock	375 m
3 oz	sultanas	75

*Vermicelli, very thin noodles, are available in the pasta section of most supermarkets. I prefer rice vermicelli, sometimes called rice sticks, which are clear, very thin noodles often sold in the Chinese food section of the supermarket.

Right:
Beetroot and Yogurt Soup (page 41), Chilled Carrot and Coriander Soup (page 44), Asparagus and Potato Bisque (page 31)

In large pot of boiling water, cook vermicelli according to package directions or for 3 to 5 minutes, just until al dente (tender but firm). Don't overcook, because noodles become mushy. Rinse under cold water; drain well and set aside.

On a pie plate, bake pine nuts in 350°F (180°C) Gas Mark 4 oven for 5 minutes or until golden. Set aside.

Curry Dressing: In saucepan of boiling water, blanch pearl onions for 3 minutes; drain. Let cool slightly, then peel.

In saucepan, heat oil over medium heat. Add curry powder, coriander, cardamom and turmeric; cook for 3 minutes, stirring occasionally. Add garlic, pearl onions, stock and raisins. Simmer for 5 minutes or until onions are tender. Remove from heat and let cool.

Toss noodles with dressing. (Salad can be covered and refrigerated for up to 1 day.) Just before serving, add pine nuts and parsley; toss well. Makes 10 servings.

Salmon is an excellent source
of omega 3 polyunsaturated
fatty acids, which some studies
have found help to lower
blood pressure and to reduce
the risk of heart disease.

PER SERVING	
calories	230
g fat	7
g protein	17
g carbohydrate	23
Good: iron	
Excellent: niacin	

Left:
Mange Tout and Red Pepper
Buffet Salad (page 48), Carrot
and Cracked-Wheat Salad
with Yogurt and Herb Dressing
(page 54), Italian Rice and
Mozzarella Salad (page 51),
Pasta Salad with Salmon and
Green Beans (page 57)

Pasta Salad with Salmon and Green Beans

This is one of my favourite pasta salads. Fresh dill adds a
wonderful flavour, but if not available, use fresh basil to taste. In
a pinch, use 1 tsp (5 ml) dried basil or dill plus 2 oz (50 g) finely
chopped fresh parsley. (Recipe pictured opposite.)

$\frac{1}{2}$ lb	small pasta shells or macaroni	225 g
$\frac{1}{4}$ lb	green beans	100 g
$2\frac{1}{2}$ oz	cottage cheese	60 g
$2\frac{1}{2}$ oz	low-fat natural yogurt	60 g
1 tbsp	fresh lemon juice	15 ml
$\frac{3}{4}$ oz	coarsely chopped fresh dill	20 g
2	cans (7.75 oz [220 g]) salmon, drained	2
	freshly ground pepper	
	lettuce	

In large pot of boiling water, cook pasta until al dente (tender
but firm). Drain and rinse under cold water; drain again and set
aside.

Cut green beans into $1\frac{1}{2}$–inch (4 cm) lengths and blanch in
boiling water for 2 minutes. Drain and rinse under cold water;
drain thoroughly and set aside.

In food processor or through sieve, purée cottage cheese.
Combine with yogurt and lemon juice; mix well.

In bowl, combine pasta, green beans, yogurt mixture and dill;
stir to mix. Discard skin from salmon and break into chunks;
add to salad and stir gently to mix. Add pepper to taste. Line
serving plates with lettuce leaves and mound salad on top.
Makes 8 servings.

Tortellini with Tuna Salad

Pasta salads are great for lunch, picnics, buffets and light suppers. You don't really need a recipe; just add any of the usual salad ingredients, such as cooked or raw vegetables, (except for lettuces) to cooked noodles or any type of pasta and toss with a dressing.

$\frac{3}{4}$ lb	tortellini	300 g
6 oz	frozen peas	150 g
$\frac{1}{2}$	red pepper, diced	$\frac{1}{2}$
$2\frac{1}{2}$ oz	chopped red onion	60 g
1	tin (6.5 oz [184 g]) tuna, packed in water, drained	1
1	can (14 oz [398 g]) artichokes, drained and quartered (optional)	1
$\frac{3}{4}$ oz	chopped fresh parsley	20 g
$\frac{1}{2}$ oz	chopped fresh basil (or 2 tsp [10 ml] dried)	12 g

Dressing

1	clove garlic, minced	1
1 tsp	Dijon mustard	5 ml
3 tbsp	lemon juice or white wine vinegar	45 ml
4 tbsp	orange juice	60 ml
3 tbsp	olive oil	45 ml
$2\frac{1}{2}$ oz	low-fat natural yogurt	60 g
$\frac{1}{2}$ oz	finely chopped fresh basil	12 g
	salt and freshly ground pepper	

PER SERVING	
calories	278
g fat	6
g protein	16
g carbohydrate	40

Good: fibre, iron
Excellent: vitamin C, niacin

Grated Carrot and Pea Salad
For a quick, easy high-fibre salad combine cooked frozen peas, grated carrot, diced celery, chopped spring onion and fresh parsley. Mix equal parts of sour cream and yogurt, add $\frac{1}{2}$ tsp (2 ml) or more Dijon mustard, and freshly ground pepper to taste; mix lightly with carrot mixture.
    Sliced water chestnuts or artichoke hearts are good additions.

Peas — fresh, frozen or canned are an excellent source of dietary fibre. Add them to soups, salads, stir-frys and pasta dishes.

In large pot of boiling water, cook tortellini until al dente (tender but firm); drain and rinse under cold water. Drain thoroughly. Thaw peas under cold water.
    In salad bowl, combine pasta, peas, red pepper, onion, tuna, artichokes (if using), parsley and basil; toss lightly to mix.
    Dressing: In blender, food processor or bowl, combine garlic, mustard, lemon and orange juice; mix well. With machine running or while mixing, gradually add oil. Add yogurt, basil, and salt and pepper to taste; mix. Pour over salad and toss to mix. Cover and refrigerate for up to 2 days. Makes 8 servings.

Pasta and Fresh Vegetable Salad

This is the kind of salad I often make during the summer using whatever vegetables I have on hand. It's great with cold meats, salmon or tuna salad, poached fish, or chicken and sliced tomatoes. It keeps well for a few days in the refrigerator and is fine for lunches or picnics.

$\frac{1}{2}$ lb	pasta shells or twirls	225 g
1	green pepper, chopped	1
4	small carrots, thinly sliced	4
4	spring onions, chopped	4
6	radishes, sliced	6
$\frac{1}{2}$	cauliflower, cut in small florets	$\frac{1}{2}$
$1\frac{1}{2}$ oz	chopped fresh parsley	40 g

Italian Vinaigrette Dressing

2 fl oz	cider or tarragon vinegar	60 ml
2 fl oz	vegetable oil	60 ml
2 fl oz	orange juice	60 ml
2 tsp	Dijon mustard	10 ml
1 tbsp	grated Parmesan cheese	15 ml
1	clove garlic, crushed	1
1 tsp	each dried basil and oregano	5 ml
	salt	
	freshly ground pepper	

PER SERVING	
calories	165
g fat	6
g protein	5
g carbohydrate	24

Excellent: vitamin A, vitamin C, fibre

In large pot of boiling water, cook pasta until al dente (tender but firm). Drain and rinse under cold water; drain thoroughly.

In large bowl, combine cooked pasta, green pepper, carrots, onions, radishes, cauliflower and parsley.

Italian Vinaigrette Dressing: In bowl or food processor, combine vinegar, oil, orange juice, mustard, cheese, garlic, basil, oregano, salt and pepper; mix well. Pour over salad and toss to mix. Cover and refrigerate for up to 2 days. Makes 10 servings.

When cooking pasta for dinner, cook extra to use another day in a salad. Rinse cooked pasta under cold water to prevent it sticking together.

Light Supper

Fettuccine and Mussel Salad (page 60)
Sliced tomatoes with fresh basil
Homemade Crispbread (page 153)
Fresh strawberries

PER SERVING	
calories	308
g fat	8
g protein	15
g carbohydrate	43
Good: iron	
Excellent: fibre, vitamin C, niacin	

For other salad recipes see

Beetroot Vinaigrette, Old-Fashioned Pickled Beetroots (page 139)
Tomato, Broccoli and Pasta Salad (page 108)
Warm Vegetable Salad with Tomato and Onion Dressing (page 27)

Fettuccine and Mussel Salad

This easy-to-make salad is delicious with any kind of cooked pasta, from linguine to spaghetti to shells. Serve as a first course or with soup for a light dinner or as part of a buffet supper.

$\frac{3}{4}$ lb	fettuccine	300
3 lb	mussels	1.5 k
2 fl oz	water	60 m
7 oz	frozen peas, thawed	180
1	red or green pepper, chopped	
4	spring onions, chopped	
1 oz	chopped fresh parsley	25
2 fl oz	lemon juice	60 m
2 fl oz	vegetable or olive oil	60 m
2	cloves garlic, crushed	
	salt and freshly ground pepper	

In large pot of boiling water, cook fettuccine until al dente (tender but firm). Drain and rinse under cold water; drain thoroughly and set aside. You should have about 2 pt (1¼ lit).

Scrub mussels under cold running water and remove any hairy beards. Discard any that do not close when tapped. In large heavy saucepan, combine water and mussels. Cover and bring to boil over high heat; reduce heat and simmer for 5 to 8 minutes or until mussels open. Discard any that do not open. Let cool; reserve 4 fl oz (100 ml) cooking liquid and remove mea from shells.

In large salad bowl, combine fettuccine, mussels, peas, pepper, spring onions and parsley.

In small bowl or food processor, combine reserved mussel cooking liquid, lemon juice, oil and garlic; mix well. Pour over pasta mixture and toss to mix. Season with salt and pepper to taste. Cover and refrigerate until chilled. Makes 8 servings.

Fresh Tomato and Chive Dressing

This light dressing is particularly good on appetizer salads or spooned over cold cooked vegetables. In order to get the most fibre, don't peel or seed tomatoes. If you prepare the dressing in advance, add cheese just before serving.

2	medium tomatoes, diced	2
2 tbsp	cider or white wine vinegar	30 ml
2 tbsp	vegetable oil	30 ml
2 tsp	Dijon mustard	10 ml
1	clove garlic, crushed (optional)	1
3 tbsp	chopped chives or spring onion	45 ml
	freshly ground pepper	
1½ oz	crumbled feta cheese	40 g

PER 1 tbsp (15 ml) SERVING	
calories	12
g fat	1
g protein	0
g carbohydrate	0

In small bowl, combine tomatoes, vinegar, oil, mustard, garlic (if using), chives, and pepper to taste; mix well. Cover and refrigerate for up to 3 days. Just before serving, stir in cheese. Makes ¾ pt (500 ml).

Mustard and Garlic Vinaigrette

By adding water to reduce the fat and mustard and garlic to increase the flavour the result is a lower-calorie, yet very tasty dressing.

PER 1 tbsp (15 ml) SERVING	
calories	50
g fat	5
g protein	0
g carbohydrate	0.5

1	clove garlic, crushed	
2 tsp	Dijon mustard	10 m
2 tbsp	lemon juice	30 m
2 fl oz	water	60 m
½ tsp	granulated sugar	2 m
2 fl oz	vegetable oil	60 m
1 tsp	grated Parmesan cheese	5 m
	freshly ground pepper	

In blender, food processor or mixing bowl, combine garlic, mustard, lemon juice, water and sugar; mix well. With machine running or while mixing, gradually add oil. Add Parmesan; season with pepper to taste. Makes about ¼ pt (150 ml).

Compare

per tbsp (15 ml)	g fat	calories
This recipe	5	50
Standard vinaigrette recipe (4 parts oil; 1 part vinegar)	10	95

Walnut Oil Vinaigrette
Prepare Mustard and Garlic Vinaigrette but substitute walnut oil for vegetable oil and omit Parmesan cheese.

PER 1 tbsp (15 ml) SERVING	
calories	17
g fat	1
g protein	0.5
g carbohydrate	1

Variations

Blue Cheese Dressing
Add 2 tbsp (30 ml) crumbled
blue cheese.

Fresh Herb
Add 2 tbsp (30 ml) chopped
fresh dill, or 1 tbsp (15 ml)
chopped fresh basil, or 2 tsp
(10 ml) chopped fresh
tarragon.

Watercress
Add 1½ oz (40 g) chopped
watercress leaves.

Onion or Chive
Add 2 tbsp (30 ml) chopped
green onions or chives (or to
taste).

Celery
Add 1 tsp (5 ml) celery seed
and 2 tbsp (30 ml) chopped
celery leaves. (Use on
coleslaw.)

Cumin
Add ½ tsp (2 ml) dried ground
cumin.

Curry
Add 1 tsp (5 ml) curry powder.

Tomato
Add 2 tbsp (30 ml) tomato
purée.

Ranch-Style Buttermilk Dressing

Even though this dressing contains mayonnaise, it is much lower in fat and calories than most creamy dressings. Use it with tossed green salads, coleslaw or chilled cooked vegetables.

8 fl oz	buttermilk	250 ml
4 tbsp	low-calorie mayonnaise	60 ml
1	small clove garlic, crushed	1
½ tsp	granulated sugar	2 ml
½ tsp	dried dillweed	2 ml
¼ tsp	dry mustard	1 ml
Pinch	freshly ground pepper	Pinch
2 tbsp	chopped fresh parsley	30 ml

In small bowl or jar, combine buttermilk, mayonnaise, garlic, sugar, dillweed, mustard, pepper and parsley; mix well. Cover and refrigerate for up to 4 days. Makes 12 fl oz (375 ml).

PER 2 tbsp (30 ml) SERVING	
calories	55
g fat	4
g protein	1
g carbohydrate	5

Yogurt and Orange Dressing

This quick and easy dressing is delicious with a fruit salad.

6 oz	low-fat natural yogurt	150
2 tbsp	vegetable oil	30 m
2 tbsp	frozen orange-juice concentrate	30 m
1 tbsp	packed brown sugar	15 m
1 tsp	grated orange rind	5 m

In small bowl, combine yogurt, oil, orange juice, sugar and orange rind; mix thoroughly. Cover and refrigerate for up to 2 days. Makes approximately 8 fl oz (250 ml).

Creamy Herb Dressing

Use this light yet creamy dressing on pasta salads, vegetable salads and lettuce salads. Because the flavours develop upon standing, if you want to use the dressing immediately increase the mustard, oregano and basil to $\frac{1}{2}$ tsp (2 ml) each or more to taste.

PER 2 tbsp (30 ml) SERVING (made with cottage cheese)	
calories	22
g fat	0.5
g protein	3
g carbohydrate	2

3 oz	cottage cheese or low-fat soft cheese	75
2½ oz	low-fat natural yogurt	60
¼ tsp	Dijon mustard	1 m
¼ tsp	each dried oregano and basil (or 1 tbsp [15 ml] chopped fresh)	1 m
	salt and freshly ground pepper	

In blender or food processor, process cottage cheese until smooth. Add yogurt, mustard, oregano and basil. Add salt and pepper to taste; process to mix. Cover and refrigerate for 4 hours or up to 3 days. Makes 4 fl oz (125 ml).

Salads

Salads aren't always a light meal when it comes to considering the fat content. Lunch of a roll and salad can add up to more than half the amount of fat you need in a day.

The amount of dressing (2 tbsp [30 ml]) used in this chart is a conservative amount of salad dressing. If you like a lot of dressing, you could easily be using double this amount. If this is the case you could be eating 30 g of fat just in a salad, which is about half the daily fat requirement for someone consuming 1800 calories a day.

If you spread your bread or roll with 1 tbsp (15 ml) butter or margarine you are adding another 11 g of fat.

For other salad dressing recipes see

Herb Vinaigrette (Tossed Seasonal Greens, page 52)
Tomato and Onion Dressing (Warm Vegetable Salad with Tomato and Onion Dressing, page 27)
Sesame Seed Dressing (Spinach Salad with Sesame Seed Dressing, page 53)
Yogurt and Herb Dressing (Carrot and Cracked-Wheat Salad with Yogurt and Herb Dressing, page 54)
Curry Dressing (Curried Vermicelli Noodle Salad, page 56)
Mustard Vinaigrette (Tomato Broccoli and Pasta Salad, page 108)
Italian Vinaigrette Dressing (Pasta and Fresh Vegetable Salad, page 59)
Walnut Orange Dressing (Mange Tout and Red Pepper Buffet Salad, page 48).

Hidden Fat

Next time you make a salad at home or at a salad bar estimate how much dressing you use and compare to this:

per 2 tbsp (30 ml)*	g fat	calories
Mustard and Garlic Vinaigrette (page 62)	10	100
Standard home vinaigrette	20	190
Italian (shop-bought)	16	160
Italian Reduced Calorie (shop-bought)	1	12
Ranch-Style Buttermilk Dressing (page 63)	2	34
Ranch Style (shop-bought)	14	140
Blue Cheese (page 62)	4	44
Blue cheese (shop-bought)	14	142
Light blue cheese (shop-bought)	6	80
Creamy Herb Dressing (page 64)	1	22
Mayonnaise-type dressing (shop-bought)	12	120

*A portion in a small ladle or a heaping dessert spoonful

Choosing an Oil for Salad Dressings

Oils are made up of a combination of different fats; some are much more saturated than others. The flavour should also be considered when choosing an oil.

Choose

safflower   walnut   olive
sunflower   soyabean   corn
canola (has the least amount of saturated fat)
sesame (strong flavour, so use in small amounts)

Sesame oil has a distinct, strong nutty flavour and is used sparingly, usually combined with another oil as a flavouring to a stir-fry or salad dressing.

Because walnut and olive oils are heavier you can use a smaller amount and often combine them with another oil (such as safflower); these oils are nice for salads. I find corn oil unappealing for salads; it is better for cooking.

Avoid

palm oil (high in saturated fat)
coconut oil (high in saturated fat)
vegetable oil (when the kind of oil isn't stated on a container, it may be palm or coconut or cottonseed oil)

Recommended Cuts

Beef: flank, top-side, silver-side, brisket, stewing steak (lean), sirloin steak (if well trimmed), very lean mince (10% fat) and rump

Pork: choose lean cuts or those easy to trim, loin roast, leg roast, loin chops, pork steaks (choose ham and bacon less often because of their high salt and fat content)

Lamb: cuts from leg and loin section

Veal: lower in fat than beef and other red meats; all cuts are lean except those from the breast (i.e., stewing veal).

If you do buy cuts higher in fat, then choose a cooking method with which you can pour off the fat. For example, if you buy minced beef, use it in spaghetti sauce so that you can brown the meat first then pour off the fat before adding other ingredients. If you use stewing veal, make the dish a day ahead and refrigerate. The next day you can easily remove the fat that will have hardened on top of the dish.

When possible, choose lean or medium minced beef. Minced pork varies in fat content and often isn't very different from minced beef. When compared with beef, pork looks fattier because the meat is only minced once; beef is minced twice so it is more uniform in colour.

Selecting Poultry

Turkey, chicken, game hens, quail or partridge are good choices. Avoid self-basting turkeys because they are injected with saturated fats. Duck and goose are very high in fat. Removing the skin from poultry significantly reduces fat content.

MEAT AND POULTRY

People often tell me about how healthily they are eating and how their diet has changed over the years. One of the first things they say is that they don't eat red meat anymore.

Red meat has been given bad press; there is no reason to eliminate it from your diet completely. Meat is an important source of complete protein, useable iron, B vitamins (thiamin, niacin and B12) and minerals, but it also contains a high proportion of saturated fats. For this reason, the selection of meats, the size of the servings and the method of cooking become very important.

Recent studies show that beef and pork are now much leaner as farmers are slowly changing the carcass composition of the animals by breeding.

Compare		g fat*
12 oz (300 g) serving rib roast, including fat		72
6 oz (150 g) serving roast beef, including fat		36
1 tbsp (15 ml) butter or margarine (for a roll)		14
2 tbsp (30 ml) mayonnaise (for a salad)		22
	Total	72
3 oz (75 g) serving top round steak (lean only)		5
1 tsp (5 ml) butter or margarine (for a roll)		5
1 tbsp (15 ml) low calorie mayonnaise (for a salad)		5
	Total	15

*The average woman's daily fat allowance is about 70 grams a day; a rough estimate for an average man is about 100 g of fat a day.

Which meat has the most fat: beef, pork, lamb or chicken? Whether or not beef has more fat than pork is not really the issue. *What is most important is the kind of cut you buy, the way you cook it and the amount you eat.* A lean cut of pork has less fat than a prime rib roast. Pork spareribs have more fat than top round steak. Try to choose a lean cut, remove all visible fat and cook it without adding any fat.

PER SERVING	
calories	324
g fat	12
g protein	20
g carbohydrate	35
Good: fibre, iron	
Excellent: vitamin A, vitamin C, thiamin, niacin	

Family Favourite Shepherd's Pie

My mother always made shepherd's pie from leftover Sunday roast beef, gravy, and mashed potatoes. However, since we seldom have roasts, I make shepherd's pie using minced meat — either beef or pork or lamb. If you don't have leftover mashed potatoes, boil 5 medium potatoes; drain and mash with milk.

1 lb	lean minced beef or pork or lamb, or a combination of these	450 g
2	onions, chopped	2
2	cloves garlic, crushed	2
1	carrot, minced (optional)	1
3 oz	tomato purée	75 g
5 fl oz	water	150 ml
1 tsp	dried thyme	5 ml
2 tsp	Worcestershire sauce	10 ml
	freshly ground pepper	
	paprika	
1 lb	mashed potatoes	450 g

In a nonstick pan over medium heat, cook beef, stirring to break up meat, until brown; pour off fat. Add onions, garlic, and carrot (if using); cook until tender. Add tomato purée, water, thyme, Worcestershire sauce, and pepper to taste. Simmer for 5 minutes, stirring up any bits on bottom of pan.

Spoon meat mixture into baking or microwave-safe dish; spread mashed potatoes evenly on top. Sprinkle with paprika to taste. Bake in 375°F (190°C) Gas Mark 5 oven for 35 minutes or until heated through, or microwave at high (100%) power for 9 minutes. Makes 5 servings.

Beef and Tomato Stir-Fry

Make this easy, tasty dish in the summer and autumn when garden-fresh tomatoes are plentiful. Serve over rice or noodles. In winter substitute green peppers, broccoli or mange tout instead of tomatoes and cook until crisp-tender, adding water if necessary to prevent burning.

¾ lb	fillet or flank steak	300 g
2 tbsp	cornflour	30 ml
2 tbsp	sherry	30 ml
1 tbsp	soy sauce	15 ml
2 tbsp	vegetable oil	30 ml
1	onion, thinly sliced	1
2	cloves garlic, crushed	2
4	tomatoes, cut in wedges	4
4	spring onions, cut in thin 2-in (5 cm) long strips	4

Cut beef across the grain into thin strips; cut strips into 2-in (5 cm) lengths. In bowl, combine cornflour, sherry and soy sauce; mix until smooth. Add beef and toss to coat.

In wok or nonstick pan, heat oil over high heat. Add beef and stir-fry for 2 minutes; add onion and stir-fry for 1 minute or until beef is browned. Add garlic and tomatoes; stir-fry until tomatoes are heated through, 1 to 2 minutes. Stir in spring onions and serve immediately. Makes 4 servings.

PER SERVING	
calories	206
g fat	9
g protein	20
g carbohydrate	12

Good: fibre, vitamin A, iron
Excellent: niacin, vitamin C

If you're cooking for one, buy a rump steak and cut it into three portions. Use one portion for the Ginger and Garlic Marinated Rump Steak, one for the Beef and Tomato Stir-Fry (page 69, cut recipe in half) and one for the Stir-Fry for One (page 198).

PER SERVING	
calories	134
g fat	4
g protein	23
g carbohydrate	1
Good: iron	
Excellent: niacin	

Buffet

Ginger and Garlic Marinated Rump Steak (cold) (page 70)
Tossed Seasonal Greens (page 52)
Wholemeal and Oatmeal Bread (page 150)
Streusel Cake (page 160)
Apricot Yogurt Parfaits (page 162)

Most marinade recipes call for more oil than necessary. Even though the marinade is poured off before cooking, I recommend keeping the oil at a minimum.

Ginger and Garlic Marinated Rump Steak

This is a favourite in our household. If I'm organized, I try to marinate it early in the day. The steak can marinate for two days and, once cooked, it is good hot or cold. (In other words, if no one arrives home for dinner — your children get invited out and your husband has to work late — you can cook it the next day. Or, if only one person appears, you can cook it and serve the rest the next day!) If you're cooking for two, have it hot the first night and cold the second.

1	rump steak, about 1 lb (450 g)	
	Italian Herb Marinade or Ginger and Garlic Marinade (recipes follow)	

Lightly score (cut) beef about $\frac{1}{8}$-in (3 mm) deep in diagonal slashes. Place in shallow dish. Pour marinade over; cover and refrigerate for at least 2, or up to 48 hours, turning meat once or twice.

Remove meat from marinade and grill for 4 to 5 minutes on each side or to preference. Cut diagonally across the grain into thin slices. Serve hot or cold. Makes 4 servings.

Ginger and Garlic Marinade

Use also with fish, prawns, chicken, turkey, beef, pork or lamb

2 tbsp	cider vinegar	30 m
2 tbsp	water	30 m
1 tbsp	vegetable oil	15 m
1 tbsp	grated fresh root ginger (or 1 tsp [5 ml] ground ginger)	15 m
1 tsp	granulated sugar	5 m
1	clove garlic, crushed	1

Combine vinegar, water, oil, ginger, sugar and garlic; mix well. Makes about 3 fl oz (90 ml), enough for one 1 lb (450 g) steak.

Rump Steak
Rump steak is one of the
leanest cuts of beef. It's
delicious when marinated,
then grilled and cut diagonally
across the grain into thin
slices. When served this way,
it's also an economical cut of
beef because 1 lb (450 g) will
serve four people. (One
pound of porterhouse steak of
the same thickness looks very
skimpy when divided into four
portions.)

Father's Day Dinner

Ginger and Garlic Marinated
Rump Steak (page 70)
Yogurt Béarnaise Sauce
(page 138)
New Potatoes with Herbs
(page 132)
Asparagus
Strawberry Mousse (page 158)
or
Blackberries with Orange and
Honey Yogurt (page 169)
Applesauce and Raisin Squares
(page 146)

Italian Herb Marinade

Use also with beef, pork, lamb, chicken or turkey.

2 fl oz	red wine vinegar	60 ml
1 tbsp	vegetable oil	15 ml
2 tbsp	chopped fresh parsley	30 ml
1 tsp	dried marjoram or oregano (or 1 tbsp [15 ml] chopped fresh)	5 ml
1 tsp	dried thyme (or 1 tbsp [15 ml] chopped fresh)	5 ml
1	bay leaf, crumbled	1
1	small onion, finely chopped	1
2	cloves garlic, crushed	2
	freshly ground pepper	

In small bowl mix together vinegar, oil, parsley, marjoram, thyme, bay leaf, onion, garlic and pepper to taste. Makes about 3 fl oz (90 ml), enough for one 1 lb (450 g) steak.

The flavour of a stew is usually better the second day. Make it a day in advance and refrigerate. Any fat will solidify on top and can easily be removed.

PER SERVING	
calories	235
g fat	5
g protein	20
g carbohydrate	27

Good: fibre, iron
Excellent: vitamin A, vitamin C, niacin

Simple Beef and Vegetable Stew

This is the easiest stew to make and tastes wonderful. Make it on the weekend and you'll probably have enough left over for a meal during the week.

1½ lb	stewing beef	675 g
1 oz	plain flour	25 g
6	small onions	6
2	large potatoes, cut in chunks (1 lb [450 g])	2
3	large carrots, cut in chunks	3
3	cloves garlic, crushed	3
9 oz	diced turnip	230 g
1¼ pt	water	750 ml
10 fl oz	beef stock	300 ml
1	small can (7½ oz [213 g]) tomato purée	1
1 tsp	dried thyme	5 ml
½ tsp	dried oregano	2 ml
¼ tsp	freshly ground pepper	1 ml
1	bay leaf	1
½ tsp	grated orange rind (optional)	2 ml

Remove all visible fat from beef; cut beef into 1 in (2.5 cm) cubes.

In large casserole or Dutch oven, toss beef with flour. Add onions, potatoes, carrots, garlic, turnip, water, beef stock, tomato purée, thyme, oregano, pepper, bay leaf and orange rind; stir to mix.

Bake, covered, in 325°F (160°C) Gas Mark 3 oven for 3 hours, stirring occasionally (if you remember). Remove bay leaf. Makes 8 servings.

Compare	mg sodium per serving
This recipe	325
Canned beef and vegetable stew	1064

Compare	Beef Cuts and Portion Sizes			
	3 oz (75 g) portion		6 oz (150 g) portion	
Cut	g fat	calories	g fat	calories
Rib roast, roasted lean and fat	18	256	36	512
Rib roast, roasted lean only	10	196	20	392
Steak (lean and fat)	5	154	10	308
Steak (lean only)	3	144	6	288

Amount to serve

How do I know what a 3- or 4-oz portion of meat is? The easiest way is to *buy* only that much. For example, if you are cooking for 4 people, buy only 1 lb (450 g) of minced meat, stewing beef, pork chops or boneless chicken breasts. For 4 servings, buy about 1½ lb (675 g) of bone-in meats, 2 lb (1 kg) of chicken.

When you are cooking roasts or bone-in cuts it is more difficult to judge amounts; for a rough estimate, consider a 3½ oz serving of meat to be about the size of a deck of playing cards. Many adults, especially men, are used to larger meat portions than 3 oz (75 g).

How to make the recommended serving size of meat, i.e., 3 oz (75 g), not look skimpy:

*The meat portion should only take up ¼ of the dinner plate. Increase the amount and variety of vegetables you serve.

*Slice meat thinly, it will look like more. For example 3 oz (75 g) of thinly sliced rump steak will look as if there is more meat than the same weight of sirloin steak in a single piece 1 in (2.5 cm) thick.

*Choose dishes in which meat is combined with vegetables, such as stews, stir-frys and casseroles.

*Serve as a sauce over pasta — see Spaghetti Sauce recipes, page 182.

*The Food Guide (page 206) recommends we have two servings (3 oz [75 g]) of meat or meat alternatives a day. If one serving is small, for example a thin slice of meat in a sandwich at lunch, then the serving size at dinner can be larger.

Beef and Pasta Casserole

This is the type of dish to serve to a crowd. It's also perfect to take to a potluck supper or for a teenager's party.

1 lb	short pasta (penne, fusilli, rotini)	450 g
1 tsp	vegetable oil	5 ml
2 lb	lean minced beef	1 kg
3	onions, finely chopped	3
2	cloves garlic, crushed	2
$\frac{1}{2}$ lb	mushrooms, sliced	225 g
2	sticks celery, sliced	2
1	green pepper, chopped	1
1	large can (13 oz [369 g]) tomato purée	1
$1\frac{3}{4}$ pt	water	1 lit
1 tsp	each dried oregano and basil	5 ml
$\frac{1}{2}$ oz	chopped fresh parsley	12 g
1	pkg (10 oz [284 g]) fresh spinach, cooked, drained and chopped	1
1 lb	low-fat mozzarella cheese, cut in small cubes	450 g
	salt and freshly ground pepper	
2 oz	fresh bread crumbs	50 g
2 oz	freshly grated Parmesan cheese	50 g

PER SERVING	
calories	378
g fat	13
g protein	29
g carbohydrate	36

Good: fibre, riboflavin
Excellent: vitamin A, vitamin C, niacin, calcium, iron

May be prepared up to two days in advance, covered and refrigerated. Remove from refrigerator one hour before baking.

In large pot of boiling water, cook pasta until al dente (tender but firm), about 10 minutes or according to package directions. Drain and rinse under cold running water; drain and set aside.

In large nonstick pan or Dutch oven, heat oil over medium heat. Add beef, onions and garlic; cook, stirring, for a few minutes or until beef is no longer pink. Drain off fat. Add mushrooms, celery, and green pepper; cook for 5 minutes, stirring occasionally. Stir in tomato purée, water, oregano, basil and parsley; simmer, covered, for 30 minutes.

Combine meat sauce, spinach, pasta and mozzarella cheese;

season to taste with salt and pepper. Spoon into lightly greased 7 pt (4 lit) casserole. Sprinkle with bread crumbs, then Parmesan. Bake, uncovered, in 350°F (180°C) Gas Mark 4 oven for 45 minutes or until bubbly. Makes 14 servings.

Grilled Butterflied Leg of Lamb with Lemon and Garlic

I love lamb, and this is one of my favourite ways to cook it. I either barbecue or grill this cut; when it's cooked medium-rare, lamb is delicious cold the next day.

3	cloves garlic, crushed	3
$\frac{1}{2}$ tsp	grated lemon rind	2 ml
$\frac{1}{2}$ tsp	dried crushed rosemary (or 1 tbsp [15 ml] chopped fresh)	2 ml
$\frac{1}{4}$ tsp	freshly ground pepper	1 ml
2 tbsp	lemon juice	30 ml
2 tbsp	olive or vegetable oil	30 ml
1	boned and butterflied* leg of lamb (about 3 lb [1.5 kg] boned)	1

In small bowl or food processor, combine garlic, lemon rind, rosemary, pepper and lemon juice. Gradually pour in oil and mix until blended.

Trim fat from lamb. Place lamb in shallow dish; pour marinade over, turning to coat both sides. Cover and let stand at room temperature for 1 to 2 hours or refrigerate overnight (bring to room temperature before cooking).

Remove lamb from marinade, reserving marinade. On greased grill 4 in (10 cm) from hot coals (at high setting if a gas barbecue), or under grill, cook lamb for 15 minutes, brushing with marinade several times. Turn and cook for 12 minutes longer or until meat is pink inside.

Remove from heat and let stand for 10 minutes. To serve, slice thinly across the grain. Makes 8 servings.

* Butterflied legs of lamb are boned then cut open, but not all the way through, so the meat can be spread apart like two butterfly wings. Be sure to trim all fat from lamb.

PER SERVING (based on using only lean part of lamb)	
calories	196
g fat	10
g protein	26
g carbohydrate	1
Good: iron	
Excellent: niacin	

Cooking Methods to Reduce Fat

*Most of the time, don't fry meats — instead, grill, stew, stir-fry, braise, roast on a rack.

*If you are going to fry, use a nonstick pan and use as little unsaturated margarine or vegetable (not palm or coconut) oil as possible.

*Make a stew one day in advance; cover and refrigerate. When cold, remove fat that has solidified on top.

Lamb Tenderloins with Rosemary and Peppercorns

Fork-tender lamb tenderloins or loins, often available in the frozen food section of the supermarket, are a special treat and one of the leanest cuts of lamb.

SERVING	
calories	170
g fat	7
g protein	25
g carbohydrate	0
Good: iron	
Excellent: niacin	

1 lb	lamb tenderloins or loins	450 g
1½ tsp	dried peppercorns, crushed (¼ tsp [1 ml] freshly ground)	7 ml
1 tbsp	fresh rosemary (or 1 tsp [5 ml]dried)	15 ml
2 tbsp	chopped fresh mint (optional)	30 ml
2	cloves garlic, crushed	2
2 tbsp	dry sherry or red wine vinegar	30 ml
1 tbsp	light soy sauce	15 ml

Place lamb in shallow dish.

In small bowl, combine peppercorns, rosemary, mint, garlic, sherry and soy sauce; mix well and pour over lamb. Cover and marinate at room temperature for 30 minutes or refrigerate for at least 1, or up to 6, hours.

Remove from marinade. Grill 3 to 4 minutes for tenderloins; 6 minutes for loins or until meat is still pink inside, turning once or twice. Cut diagonally into thin slices. Makes 4 servings.

Lamb tenderloins and loins cook quickly and are best served rare or medium-rare. Be careful not to overcook as they will be too dry and sometimes tough.

Compare	per 4 oz (100 g) serving	
Grilled Lemon-Garlic Leg of Lamb using:	g fat	calories
Lamb leg, lean and fat	25	354
Lamb leg, lean only	10	196

Pork Chops with Rosemary and Orange

This fast and easy recipe also works well using veal or turkey escalopes. For my son (who doesn't like sauces), I don't pour any over his serving. My daughter quietly scrapes the rosemary off hers. My husband and I like it the way it is, so everyone is happy.

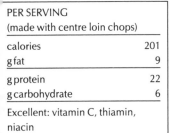

PER SERVING (made with centre loin chops)	
calories	201
g fat	9
g protein	22
g carbohydrate	6
Excellent: vitamin C, thiamin, niacin	

1 lb	fast-fry or thinly sliced pork chops	450 g
2	oranges	2
2 tsp	unsaturated margarine	10 ml
2 tsp	dried rosemary	10 ml
	salt and freshly ground pepper	

Trim fat from pork chops. Peel and slice one orange; squeeze juice from other and set aside.

Heat heavy-bottomed or nonstick pan over high heat; add margarine and heat until sizzling. Add pork chops and cook for about 2 minutes or until brown on bottom; turn. Sprinkle with rosemary, and salt and pepper to taste. Cook until brown on other side. Remove chops to side plate.

Add reserved orange juice and slices; cook for 1 to 2 minutes, stirring to scrape up brown bits on bottom of pan. To serve, arrange chops on plates and pour juice and orange slices over. Makes 4 servings.

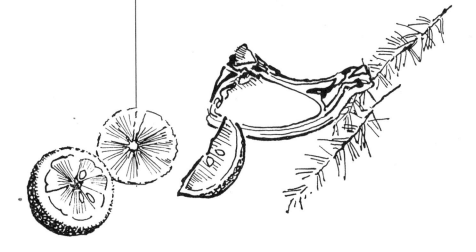

Brochette of Pork with Lemon and Herb Marinade

Herbs and lemon add tangy flavour to this easy-to-prepare pork dish. Use pork tenderloin or any other lean cut of pork. Courgettes or blanched slices of carrot can be used instead of the vegetables here.

	PER SERVING	
calories		235
g fat		12
g protein		23
g carbohydrate		8

Good: fibre, riboflavin, iron
Excellent: vitamin C, thiamin, niacin

1 lb	boneless lean pork	450
	grated rind and juice of 1 lemon	
2	large cloves garlic, crushed	
2 tsp	dried basil (or 2 tbsp [30 ml] fresh)	10 m
1 tsp	dried thyme (or 1 tbsp [15 ml] fresh)	5 m
2 tbsp	chopped fresh parsley	30 m
1 tbsp	vegetable or olive oil	15 m
1	green pepper, cut in squares	
2	onions, quartered and separated into pieces	
16	cherry tomatoes or fresh pineapple chunks	1(

Pineapple chunks canned in their own juice can be used instead of fresh pineapple.

Cut pork into 1 in (2.5 cm) cubes. In bowl, combine lemon rind and juice, garlic, basil, thyme, parsley and oil. Add pork and toss to coat well. Cover and marinate in refrigerator for 4 hours or overnight.

Alternately thread pork, green pepper, onions and cherry tomatoes or pineapple onto skewers. On greased grill about 4 in (10 cm) over hot coals, or under grill, cook brochettes, turning often, for 15 minutes or until pork is no longer pink inside. Makes 4 servings.

Cauliflower and Ham Gratin

Ham and cauliflower are a wonderul combination. Dill adds extra flavour and red pepper adds colour and crunch.

$\frac{1}{2}$	cauliflower	$\frac{1}{2}$
$1\frac{1}{2}$ tbsp	unsaturated margarine	20 ml
2 tbsp	plain flour	30 ml
8 fl oz	skimmed milk	250 ml
1 oz	freshly grated Parmesan cheese	25 g
1 oz	grated low-fat mozzarella cheese	25 g
$\frac{1}{2}$ oz	chopped fresh dill*	12 g
	freshly ground pepper	
2 oz	diced cooked ham	50 g
$\frac{1}{2}$	red pepper, coarsely chopped	$\frac{1}{2}$
1 oz	fresh bread crumbs	25 g

Cut cauliflower into florets, about 2 in (5 cm) pieces. In large pot of boiling water, blanch cauliflower for 5 minutes or until tender-crisp; drain and set aside.

In saucepan, melt margarine; add flour and cook over low heat, stirring, for 1 minute. Pour in milk and bring to simmer, stirring constantly. Simmer, stirring, for 2 minutes. Add Parmesan and mozzarella cheeses, dill, and pepper to taste; cook, stirring, until cheese melts.

In lightly greased 11 by 7 in (2 lit) shallow baking dish, arrange cauliflower, ham and pepper; pour sauce evenly over. Sprinkle with bread crumbs. Bake in 375°F (190°C) Gas Mark 5 oven for 30 minutes or until bubbly. Makes 4 servings.

*If fresh dill is unavailable, use 1 oz (25 g) fresh parsley plus 1 tsp (5 ml) dried dillweed.

PER SERVING

calories	219
g fat	10
g protein	15
g carbohydrate	18

Good: fibre, vitamin A, thiamin
Excellent: vitamin C, niacin, calcium

Nutrition Notes

Because ham is very high in salt, it shouldn't be used very often. When you do use it, try to make a little go a long way, as in this cauliflower dish. Don't add any salt.

Use the remaining cauliflower in stir-frys, in salads or soup.

Compare

Ham Dinner 1 (29% of calories from fat)	g fat	calories
Cauliflower and Ham Gratin (page 79)	10.1	219
Green beans	0.1	17
Sliced tomatoes	0.1	12
Wholemeal bun	1.0	90
Margarine (1 tsp [5 ml])	3.6	34
Milk, skimmed (½ pt [300 ml])	0	90
Totals	15.0	461

Ham Dinner 2 (47% of calories from fat)	g fat	calories
Ham steak	8.7	187
Cauliflower	0.1	14
with cheese sauce	9.9	126
Green beans	0.1	17
Wholemeal bun	1.0	90
Butter (1 tsp [5 ml])	3.6	34
Milk, whole (½ pt [300 ml])	9	159
Totals	32.4	627

The Average Fat Content of Common Cuts of Raw Meat, Poultry and Game

High-fat meats
(fat content 31–40% of raw weight)
Duck — including skin
Streaky bacon
Back bacon
Best end of lamb
Belly of pork
Loin of lamb

Moderately high-fat meats
(fat content 21–30% of raw weight)
Loin of pork
Scrag and middle neck of lamb
Shoulder of lamb
Goose
Fore rib of beef
Sirloin steak — lean and fat
Leg of pork

Moderate-fat meats
(fat content 11–20% of raw weight)
Leg of lamb
Chicken — including skin
Ox tongue
Minced beef
Rump steak — lean and fat
Pigeon

Topside of beef
Stewing steak
Lambs liver

Low-fat meats
(fat content 5–10% of raw weight)
Pheasant
Ox liver
Partridge
Calves liver
Turkey — meat and skin
Pigs liver
Venison
Chicken liver
Lambs hearts

Very low-fat meats
(fat content less than 5% of raw weight)
Duck — flesh only
Chicken — flesh only
Grouse — flesh only
Rabbit
Lambs kidney
Pigs kidney
Veal — lean
Ox kidney
Turkey — flesh only

NB. The meats are arranged in descending order of fat content within each category. The source of information is *McCance and Widdowson's Composition of Foods* and will not include any changes in the fat content of meats brought about by the use of leaner breeds or new butchery techniques.

Barbecued Lemon Chicken

This simple way to cook chicken is one of my husband's favourites — the chicken is moist and juicy and very delicious.

PER SERVING	
calories	148
g fat	4
g protein	27
g carbohydrate	0
Excellent: niacin	

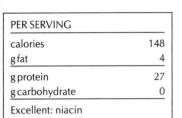

4	boneless chicken breasts	4
	juice of 1 lemon	
2 tsp	olive oil	10 ml
1	clove garlic, crushed	1
½ tsp	dried oregano	2 ml
Pinch	cayenne pepper	Pinch

Remove skin from chicken. In shallow dish, arrange chicken in single layer.

In small dish, combine lemon juice, oil, garlic, oregano and cayenne; mix well. Pour over chicken and turn to coat both sides. Let stand at room temperature for 20 minutes or cover and refrigerate up to 6 hours.

On a pre-heated greased grill, or over barbecue coals cook chicken for 4 to 5 minutes on each side or until meat is no longer pink inside. Makes 4 servings.

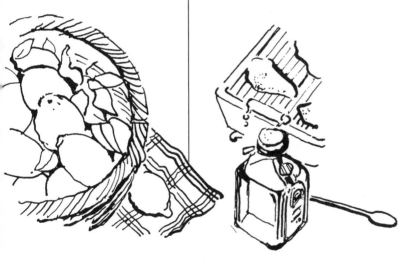

Grilled Tandoori Chicken

This Indian yogurt-and-spice marinade makes the chicken moist and full of flavour. Serve with rice and a green vegetable such as asparagus, green beans or broccoli or see the Summer Barbecue menu on this page.

PER SERVING	
calories	174
g fat	10
g protein	20
g carbohydrate	2
Good: vitamin C	
Excellent: niacin	

1½ tsp	Dijon mustard	7 ml
2 tbsp	vegetable oil	30 ml
2½ oz	low-fat natural yogurt	60 g
1½ tsp	fresh root ringer, crushed	7 ml
¼ tsp	cumin seeds	1 ml
¼ tsp	coriander seeds	1 ml
¼ tsp	ground turmeric	1 ml
2 tbsp	lemon juice	30 ml
2 tbsp	chopped canned green chilli or 1 fresh green chilli, seeded and chopped	30 ml
1	chicken, cut in pieces (about 2½ lb [1.25 kg]) or chicken breasts	1

Summer Barbecue

Grilled Tandoori Chicken (page 82)
New Potatoes with Herbs (page 132)
Sliced tomatoes with basil
Blackcurrant Sorbet (page 164)
Microwave Oatmeal Squares (page 187)

Place mustard in mixing bowl or food processor; add oil, drop by drop, whisking or processing until well blended. Stir in yogurt; set aside.

Using mortar and pestle, spice grinder or coffee grinder, pound or grind root ginger, cumin and coriander seeds, and turmeric to form a paste; add lemon juice and mix well. Stir into yogurt mixture along with chopped chilli.

Remove skin from chicken. Using knife, make very small cuts in meat. Arrange in shallow dish or place in plastic bag; pour yogurt-spice mixture over chicken and stir to coat all pieces. Cover and refrigerate for at least 8 hours or up to 24 hours.

On greased barbecue 4 to 6 in (10 to 15 cm) from hot coals, or under grill, cook chicken for 15 to 20 minutes on each side (15 minutes if top is down on barbecue) or until chicken is tender and juices run clear when chicken is pierced with fork. Watch carefully and turn to prevent burning. Makes 6 servings.

Curried Chicken Crepes

This is a delicious dish to consider when you want a make-ahead dish for brunch, lunch or dinner. If you keep crepes in your freezer and have any leftover cooked chicken or turkey, these can be a quick and easy dinner. Cooked turkey, prawns or pork can be used instead of chicken.

2 tsp	unsaturated margarine	10 ml
$\frac{1}{2}$	medium onion, chopped	$\frac{1}{2}$
2 oz	diced celery	50 g
1 tbsp	plain flour	15 ml
$1\frac{1}{2}$ tsp	curry powder (or to taste)	7 ml
	salt	
4 fl oz	chicken stock	125 ml
9 oz	diced cooked chicken (about $\frac{3}{4}$ lb [300 g] uncooked boneless chicken breasts)	230 g
$2\frac{1}{2}$ oz	sour cream	60 g
$2\frac{1}{2}$ oz	low-fat natural yogurt	60 g
8	Basic Crepes (recipe page 154)	8

Garnish

	Yogurt, chutney, green grapes	

In saucepan, melt margarine; over medium heat cook onion and celery, stirring, until onion is softened. Add flour, curry powder and salt; cook, stirring, for 1 minute.

Whisk in chicken stock and bring to simmer while whisking. Reduce heat to low and simmer, stirring, for 2 minutes. Remove from heat and stir in chicken, sour cream and yogurt. Taste and add more curry powder if desired.

Place 2 or 3 large spoonfuls of chicken mixture across centre of each crepe. Roll up and place seam-side-down in lightly greased shallow baking dish.

Bake in 375°F (190°C) Gas Mark 5 oven for 20 minutes or microwave at high (100%) power for 2 minutes or until heated through. Top each serving with spoonful of yogurt and another of chutney; garnish plate with grapes. Makes 4 servings of 2 crepes each.

PER 2 CRÊPES	
calories	244
g fat	7
g protein	25
g carbohydrate	18
Excellent: niacin	

Old-Fashioned Chicken or Turkey Pot Pie

If you have leftover cooked chicken or turkey, and any crisp-cooked vegetables such as carrots, green beans, courgettes or leeks, combine them with sliced fresh mushrooms, frozen peas and Cream Sauce (recipe page 137). Season with touch of tarragon and sherry; spoon into baking dish.

Cover with mashed potatoes and bake in 375°F (190°C) Gas Mark 5 oven for 30 minutes or until hot and bubbly and potatoes are golden.

Note: Using mashed potatoes instead of pastry as a topping for a chicken or meat pie reduces the fat by about half.

Curried Chicken and Tomato Casserole

For an easy yet elegant dinner, serve small dishes of raisins, peanuts, coconut, chutney and yogurt, plus rice, along with this casserole. For a particularly delicious fresh flavour, grind the cumin and coriander seeds just before using. You can, however substitute 2 tbsp (30 ml) curry powder or more to taste, for the cumin and coriander seeds, turmeric, aniseed and hot pepper flakes. Don't substitute canned tomatoes. The Sliced Cucumbers with Chives, Yogurt and Basil (page 50) is particularly nice with this.

	PER SERVING	
calories		198
g fat		8
g protein		20
g carbohydrate		13
Good: calcium, iron		
Excellent: vitamin C, niacin		

Make-Ahead Dinner Party

Spiced Meatballs with Coriander Dip (page 23)
Tossed Seasonal Greens (page 52)
Curried Chicken and Tomato Casserole (page 84)
Bulgur Pilaf with Apricots and Raisins (page 132)
Sliced Cucumbers with Chives, Yogurt and Basil (page 50)
Oranges in Grand Marnier (page 171)
Easy Oat Bran and Date Biscuits (page 148)

Recipe can be prepared in advance, cooled, covered and refrigerated for up to 2 days. To reheat, cook over medium heat, stirring occasionally, for about 20 minutes, or place uncovered in 350°F (180°C) Gas Mark 4 oven for 35 to 45 minutes or until heated through.

3 lb	chicken pieces (breast, thighs)	1.5 kg
2 tbsp	unsaturated margarine	30 ml
4	medium onions, chopped	4
3 tbsp	fresh root ginger, grated	45 ml
2 fl oz	water	60 ml
5	cloves garlic, crushed	5
2 tbsp	cumin seeds, ground	30 ml
2 tbsp	coriander seeds, ground	30 ml
2 tbsp	turmeric	30 ml
1 tsp	aniseed	5 ml
¼ tsp	hot pepper flakes (or to taste)	1 ml
4	large tomatoes, seeded and coarsely chopped	4
14 oz	low-fat natural yogurt	350 g
	salt and pepper	
1 tsp	garam masala*	5 ml
½ oz	chopped fresh coriander	12 g

Cut any visible fat from chicken and remove skin.

In large pan, heat margarine over medium-high heat; brown chicken pieces a few at a time and remove to plate. Add onions and cook for 3 minutes or until tender, stirring often. Add root ginger, water, garlic, cumin, coriander, turmeric, aniseed and hot pepper flakes; mix well and simmer for 1 minute. Add tomatoes and simmer for 2 minutes. Stir in yogurt.

Return chicken, including any juices, to pan and stir gently.

To Truss a Chicken
Use a cotton string to tie the legs and wings close to the body. This prevents the legs and wings from becoming overcooked and dried out before the rest of the chicken is cooked.

Season with salt and pepper to taste; add more hot pepper flakes if desired. Cover and simmer for 25 to 30 minutes or until chicken is tender and cooked through.

Just before serving, stir in garam masala and chopped coriander. Makes 10 servings.

*Buy garam masala at ethnic food shops, or make this version by using a spice grinder or coffee grinder to combine 4 peppercorns, 2 cardamom seeds, 2 cloves, $\frac{1}{2}$ in (1 cm) piece cinnamon stick, pinch each of cumin seeds and grated nutmeg.

Compare		
per serving	g fat	calories
This recipe including chicken skin	12	247
This recipe without chicken skin	8	198

Tarragon-Roasted Chicken

This is a delicious and easy way to cook chicken. Be sure to remove the skin when carving as it has a large amount of fat.

2	cloves garlic	2
1	chicken (about 3 lb [1.5 kg])	1
2 tsp	dried tarragon	10 ml
2 fl oz	white wine	60 ml
1 tbsp	vegetable oil	15 ml

Cut 1 garlic clove in half. Rub cut sides on outside of chicken; place garlic in chicken cavity. Sprinkle half the tarragon in chicken cavity. Truss chicken with string and place in roasting pan.

Crush remaining garlic and combine with remaining tarragon, wine and oil; drizzle over chicken. Roast in 350°F (180°C) Gas Mark 4 oven, basting frequently, for $1\frac{1}{4}$ hours or until juices run clear when chicken is pierced with fork. Makes 6 servings.

PER SERVING	
calories	155
g fat	6
g protein	23
g carbohydrate	80
Excellent: niacin	

PER SERVING	
calories	59
g fat	1
g protein	2
g carbohydrate	2
Good: fibre	

Variations

Instead of mushrooms or celery add chopped apple or pear, or chopped dried apricots; or replace half of the bread crumbs with cooked wild rice.

Stuffing a Chicken or Turkey

Stuff a bird just before cooking. If you stuff it in advance, even if you refrigerate it, the centre will take time to become cold and you run the risk of contamination. Fill cavity but don't pack it in, it will expand during cooking. Fasten closed with skewers or sew closed using a needle and string or thread.

Mushroom Onion Stuffing

This stuffing is good with chicken or turkey. Serve with cranberry sauce and nobody will notice if you don't have grav

6 oz	fresh whole wheat bread crumbs	150
4 oz	coarsely chopped mushrooms	100
4 oz	finely chopped celery	100
2	small onions, finely chopped	
1 tsp	dried thyme	5 n
1 tsp	dried sage	5 n
	freshly ground pepper	

In large bowl, combine bread crumbs, mushrooms, celery, onions, thyme, sage and pepper. Makes enough for a 6 lb (3 kg) chicken. (About 8 servings.)

Chicken and Prawn Creole

If preparing in advance, use long grain rice as some kinds of rice will get mushy when reheated. Cooked, sliced Italian sausage is a tasty addition or substitute for prawn in this dish.

$1\frac{1}{2}$ lb	boneless chicken	675 g
1 tbsp	vegetable oil	15 ml
2	onions, coarsely chopped	2
3	cloves garlic, crushed	3
1	each red and green pepper, coarsely chopped	1
1	can (28 oz [800 g]) tomatoes	1
$1\frac{3}{4}$ pt	chicken stock	1 lit
1 tsp	dried thyme	5 ml
1 tsp	dried oregano	5 ml
$\frac{1}{4}$ tsp	cayenne pepper	1 ml
1 lb	long grain rice	450 g
1 lb	medium prawns (fresh or frozen)	450 g
$\frac{3}{4}$ oz	chopped fresh parsley	20 g

Remove skin from chicken and cut into cubes. In large nonstick pan, heat oil over medium heat; cook chicken for about 3 minutes or until lightly browned. Add onions and garlic; cook for 3 minutes or until softened. Stir in peppers; add tomatoes, breaking up with back of spoon. Add stock, thyme, oregano and cayenne; bring to boil. Stir in rice; cover, reduce heat and simmer for 25 minutes or until most of the liquid is absorbed.

Meanwhile, in saucepan of boiling water, cook prawns for 3 minutes; drain. Peel and de-vein if necessary. Add prawns to rice mixture and cook for 5 minutes or until prawns are hot. Stir in parsley. Makes 8 servings.

PER SERVING

calories	321
g fat	5
g protein	30
g carbohydrate	38

Good: fibre, thiamin
Excellent: niacin, iron, vitamin C

Buffet Dinner for 16

(Double or triple recipes where needed.)

For the most flavour, cook prawns in shells then peel and de-vein (rather than peeling before cooking).

PER SERVING	
calories	220
g fat	10
g protein	24
g carbohydrate	6
Excellent: vitamin C, niacin	

Fresh Root Ginger
I love the flavour fresh ginger gives to cooked dishes and always try to have it on hand. It is far superior to ground ginger. Root ginger is usually available in the fresh-produce section in supermarkets and at Oriental grocery stores.

To store: Will keep in the refrigerator for 2 to 3 weeks, or freeze for up to 4 weeks.

To use: I usually peel the skin from the portion of root ginger I plan to use with a sharp knife or vegetable peeler, then either chop or finely grate it. I use fresh root ginger most often in stir-fry such as Szechuan Orange and Ginger Chicken (page 88), and with vegetables, such as Broccoli with Ginger and Lemon (page 119).
To substitute ground ginger in recipes calling for root ginger: Use ground ginger only if you can't find root ginger. Use about ½ tsp (2 ml) ground ginger in most recipes in this book. Taste, then add another ½ tsp (2 ml) if desired. Use ground ginger where called for in baked recipes such as biscuits.

Right:
Make-Ahead Paella (page 90)

Szechuan Orange and Ginger Chicken

This popular recipe is much easier and faster to make than it looks. Chinese dishes from the Szechuan region usually have a spicy, hot flavour; if you prefer a milder taste, use less chilli paste — the dish is delicious either way. Serve with rice. (Recipe pictured opposite page 89).

4	chicken breasts, skinned and boned (about 1lb [450 g] boneless)	4
1	green pepper	1
1	red pepper	1
1	orange	1
1 tsp	bottled chilli paste*	5 m
2 tbsp	sherry	30 m
1 tsp	granulated sugar	5 m
1 tsp	cornflour	5 m
2 tbsp	vegetable oil	30 m
1 tsp	garlic, crushed	5 m
1 tbsp	fresh root ginger, chopped	15 m

Cut chicken into 1 in (2.5 cm) squares; set aside. Halve green and red peppers and remove ribs and seeds; cut into 1 in (2.5 cm) squares.
Using vegetable peeler, remove rind from orange (orange part only, no white). Cut rind into thin julienne strips about 1½ in (4 cm) long; set aside. Squeeze orange and reserve 2 fl oz (60 ml) juice.
In small bowl, combine reserved orange juice, chilli paste, sherry, sugar and cornflour; stir until smooth.
In wok, heat oil over high heat; add chicken and stir-fry for 2 minutes or until no longer pink. Remove chicken. Add orange rind, garlic and root ginger; stir-fry for 10 seconds. Add peppers and stir-fry for 1 minute. Add chilli paste mixture and bring to boil. Return chicken to wok and stir until heated through. Makes 4 servings.

*Bottled chilli paste is available in some supermarkets and most Oriental grocery stores. You can substitute ½ tsp (2 ml) dried chilli peppers or the kind of hot chilli sauce found in Oriental grocery stores. The seeds in fresh or dried peppers are very hot; if you want a milder taste omit seeds.

Stir-Fried Chicken with Broccoli

Stir-fries are perfect last-minute dishes that can easily be stretched to accommodate extra guests. Just add more broccoli or extra vegetables and cook more rice or noodles. If you have dried Chinese mushrooms on hand, use a few of them (soaked first) instead of fresh.

1½ lb	boneless skinned chicken breasts	675 g
2 tbsp	vegetable oil	30 ml
2 tbsp	fresh root ginger, chopped	30 ml
2	onions, sliced	2
1½ lb	broccoli florets	675 g
5 oz	thinly sliced carrots	125 g
½ lb	mushrooms, sliced	225 g
6 fl oz	chicken stock	175 ml
2 tbsp	sherry	30 ml
2 tsp	soy sauce	10 ml
2 tsp	cornflour	10 ml
2 tbsp	water	30 ml
1 lb	sliced Chinese cabbage	450 g

Stir-frying

When stir-frying, it is very important to heat wok or heavy pan and have oil very hot before adding any food. If food sticks, either the wok wasn't hot enough or you need a little more oil. If food starts to stick after adding vegetables, add a little water to prevent scorching.

Cut chicken into thin strips about 1½ in (4 cm) long; set aside.

In wok or large pan, heat oil over high heat. Gradually add chicken to wok with half of the root ginger; stir-fry for 2 minutes. Remove from wok and set aside. Add onion and stir-fry for 2 minutes; set aside with chicken.

Add broccoli, carrots, mushrooms and remaining root ginger to wok; stir-fry for 2 minutes, adding a little water to prevent sticking if necessary.

Mix together chicken stock, sherry and soy sauce; pour over broccoli mixture. Cover and let steam for 2 minutes. Stir in reserved onion and chicken. Mix cornflour with water; stir into wok and bring to boil. Add Chinese cabbage; stir and cook for 1 minute or until tender crisp. Makes 8 servings.

Left:
Szechuan Orange and Ginger Chicken (page 88)

PER SERVING	
calories	309
g fat	8
g protein	31
g carbohydrate	30
Good: fibre, thiamin	
Excellent: niacin, vitamin C, iron	

Make-Ahead Paella

This is one of my favourite dishes for entertaining — it looks spectacular, tastes delicious and can be mostly prepared in advance. It's great any time of year for a sit-down dinner or special buffet. There are many versions of this Spanish speciality — do vary the seafood to your own tastes and to what's available. Saffron adds a delicate flavour and a beautiful yellow colour but is terribly expensive and sometimes hard to find. It unavailable add 1 tsp (5 ml) turmeric. (Recipe pictured opposite page 88).

12	clams (in shells)	1
1 lb	mussels (in shells)	450
2 lb	chicken breasts (or 1 lb [450 g] boneless)	1 kg
1 tbsp	vegetable oil or unsaturated margarine	15 m
½ lb	hot Spanish or Italian sausage	225
4	cloves garlic, crushed	4
12 oz	rice	375
1¼ pt	water or clam cooking liquid	750 m
4	coarsely chopped tomatoes (medium)	4
1	green pepper, cut in ½ in (1 cm) pieces	1
1	bay leaf	1
1 tsp	saffron threads	5 m
¼ tsp	ground turmeric	1 m
¼ tsp	freshly ground pepper	1 m
	cayenne pepper	
¾ lb	medium prawns, cooked peeled and de-veined*	300
6 oz	peas	150

To store mussels
Mussels will keep for 1 to 2 days in a bowl or paper bag in the refrigerator. Don't store in a plastic bag.

Scrub clams and mussels under cold running water; cut off any hairy beards from mussels. Discard any clams or mussels that do not close when tapped. Refrigerate mussels until needed. Steam clams** over boiling water until shells open (about 5 minutes); reserve cooking liquid, discard any that don't open. Refrigerate until needed.

Remove skin from chicken breasts; cut into bite-size pieces. In large nonstick pan, heat oil over medium-high heat, brown chicken. Transfer chicken to paella pan or large shallow casserole.

Add sausage to pan and cook (time will vary depending on type of sausage); remove from pan and cut into $\frac{1}{4}$ in (5 mm) thick slices; add to pan with chicken.

In same pan, cook garlic for 1 minute; stir in rice. Add clam cooking liquid or water, tomatoes, green pepper, bay leaf, saffron, turmeric, pepper, and cayenne to taste; bring to boil. Reduce heat and simmer for 15 minutes; pour over chicken.

(Recipe can be prepared ahead to this point, covered and refrigerated for up to 1 day. Return all ingredients to room temperature before continuing with recipe.)

Add mussels and bake, covered, in 425°F (220°C) Gas Mark 7 oven for 20 minutes. Stir in prawns, clams and peas; bake for 15 minutes or until heated through and mussels open (discard any mussels that don't open). Makes 8 servings.

---

*Cook prawns in boiling water for 3 minutes. Drain and cool under cold water; peel and de-vein.
**Because some clams take much longer to cook than others I cook them in advance. I cook the mussels in the rice because they cook in a short time and I want the liquid from the mussels to flavour the dish.

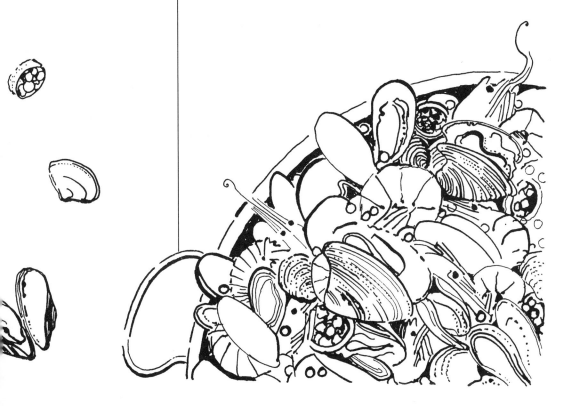

PER SERVING	
calories	162
g fat	6
g protein	25
g carbohydrate	1
Excellent: niacin	

Grilled Turkey Escalopes with Herbs and Garlic

This is a favourite dish of mine for summer entertaining. It's extremely fast and easy, yet a little different. Because turkey is tender and this is a fairly strong-flavoured marinade, it doesn't need hours of marinating and can be prepared at the last minute or an hour or two in advance. Veal escalopes can be used instead of turkey.

3	cloves garlic, crushed	
$\frac{1}{2}$ tsp	each dried thyme, rosemary and oregano	2
2 tbsp	olive oil	30
2 tbsp	lemon juice	30
	salt	
	freshly ground pepper	
1 lb	turkey escalopes*	450

In food processor or small bowl, combine garlic, thyme, rosemary, oregano, oil, lemon juice, salt, and pepper to taste; mix well. Brush over both sides of turkey. (Grill immediately or cover and let stand at room temperature for 30 minutes or refrigerate for up to 2 hours.) On lightly greased grill 4 in (10 cm) from hot coals, or under grill, cook turkey for 2 minutes on each side or just until cooked through. Makes 4 servings.

*If turkey escalopes aren't available in the shop, slice partially frozen turkey breast meat thinly, then pound between two pieces of waxed paper into $\frac{1}{4}$ in (5 mm) thick slices or use veal escalopes.

Spring Barbecue

Grilled Turkey Escalopes with Herbs and Garlic (page 92)
Asparagus
Wild rice and mushrooms
Spinach Salad with Sesame Seed Dressing (page 53)
Rhubarb and Strawberry Sorbet (page 164).

30-minute Summer Barbecue

Grilled Turkey Escalopes with Herbs and Garlic (page 92)
Corn on the cob
French bread
Sliced tomatoes
Strawberries with Raspberry Sauce (page 166)

Buying Fish

Odour and appearance are the clues to the freshness of seafood. There should be no strong fishy odour, the eyes should be bright and bulging, not shrunken into the head. The skin should spring back when pressed lightly. When I buy fish I ask the salesperson what fish came in that day and choose from these.

Storage

Wash, pat dry and cover with an airtight wrapper. Fish can be refrigerated for about two days or in a freezer as long as three months.

Cooking Fish

Fish and shellfish are naturally tender. They should be cooked for a short time at a high temperature. To determine the length of cooking time, measure the thickness of the fish at its thickest part. Cook fresh fish 10 minutes per inch of thickness, adding five minutes if wrapped in foil; frozen fish requires 20 minutes per inch, plus 10 minutes if wrapped in foil. Cooking time may vary depending on the cooking method used. Don't overcook. Overcooked fish becomes dry, tough and rubbery and loses its flavour. Fish is cooked when the flesh is opaque and it flakes easily.

Oven Steaming Fish

This method is the easiest and requires the least cleanup. Place fish on the shiny side of foil and season with lemon juice and/or herbs. Wrap fish in foil and place on baking sheet. Bake in 450°F (230°C) Gas Mark 8 oven for required time (see above), depending on thickness.

FISH

Fish is an original fast food that's easy to cook at home. Not only does it taste good but it is very nutritious. It is an excellent source of high-quality protein, and is high in vitamins A, D and B-complex, and low in fat, particularly saturated fat. Fish contains the beneficial omega-3 type of fat, which according to the latest research helps to reduce the incidence of heart disease. Most fish is lower in cholesterol than meat and poultry.

For many years shellfish were banned on diets prescribed to lower blood cholesterol. But better testing techniques now show that cholesterol isn't present in shellfish in so large an amount as to be of concern. Prawns are the shellfish that are highest in cholesterol but as long as you don't have them too often and your overall diet is low in total fat, they can still be enjoyed.

The two most important factors in preparing tasty fish are, above all, to buy good-quality fish, either fresh or frozen, and not to overcook it. You can substitute one kind of fish for another in the recipes here. Buy whatever kind is freshest and use in the recipe that appeals most to you.

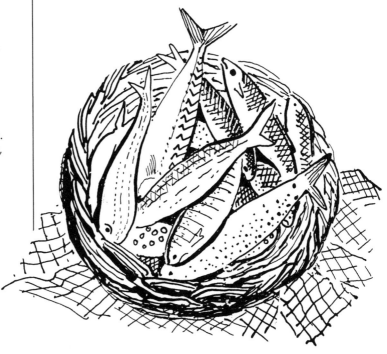

Steaming Fish
If you don't have a fish steamer you can use a wok with a lid. Place fish on a heat-proof plate. Add a small amount of water to the bottom of a wok and bring to a boil. Set two chopsticks above water level in the wok and place the plate on the chopsticks. Cover. The steam will circulate around the fish and cook it gently.

PER SERVING	
(analysis based on cod fillets)	
calories	187
g fat	8
g protein	25
g carbohydrate	3
Good: iron	
Excellent: niacin	

Herb-Breaded Fish Fillets

Here's an easy-to-make and tasty way to serve fish fillets. It's really quick if you make your bread crumbs and chop the parsley in a blender or food processor, then melt the margarine and cook the fish in a microwave.

1 lb	fish fillets	450
1 oz	fresh bread crumbs	25
1 tbsp	unsaturated margarine, melted	15 m
½ oz	chopped fresh parsley	12
1 tsp	dried thyme	5 m
	freshly ground pepper	

In shallow baking dish or microwave-safe dish, arrange fillets in single layer. Combine bread crumbs, margarine, parsley, thyme and pepper; mix well and sprinkle over fish.
Bake uncovered in 450°F (230°C) Gas Mark 8 oven for 10 minutes per inch of thickness (5 to 7 minutes per cm) for fresh fish, 20 minutes per inch (10 to 12 minutes per cm) for frozen or until fish flakes when tested with fork. Makes 4 servings.

Microwave Method
Microwave, uncovered, at high (100%) power for about 4 minutes for fresh fish or until fish flakes easily when tested with fork.

Microwaving Fish
One of the best reasons for owning a microwave is to cook fish. It take only minutes to cook and is very moist. Arrange fish in a microwave dish with the thickest part facing the outside of the dish. Season with pepper, lemon juice or herbs (always add salt after microwaving not before). Place plastic wrap over dish with a small corner turned back for steam to escape. One pound of fresh or thawed fillets in a single layer at high setting takes about 4 to 5 minutes (10 to 12 for frozen). Times will vary depending on thickness. Rotate dish during cooking.

Fish Fillets with Basil and Lemon

This is so simple and easy, yet results in the best-tasting fish. If buying frozen fillets, try to buy the kind that have been frozen in a single layer or individually wrapped. If using the kind that have been frozen in a block, defrost the fish and separate into fillets before cooking. If buying fresh, choose whatever kind of fillets are freshest. About 1 tbsp (15 ml) of any fresh herbs, such as chopped fresh dill, thyme or tarragon, can be substituted for the basil.

1 lb	fish fillets	450 g
1 tbsp	lemon juice	15 ml
2 tsp	unsaturated margarine, melted	10 ml
$\frac{1}{2}$ tsp	dried basil	2 ml
	freshly ground pepper	

Garnish

	Fresh herbs or chopped fresh parsley	

In microwave-safe or conventional baking dish, arrange fillets in a single layer. In small dish, combine lemon juice, margarine and basil; drizzle over fish. Sprinkle lightly with pepper to taste.

Bake, uncovered, in 450°F (230°C) Gas Mark 8 oven for 8 to 10 minutes (10 minutes per inch thickness for fresh fish) or until fish is opaque and flakes easily with fork. Sprinkle with fresh herbs or parsley. Makes 4 servings.

Microwave Method
Cover with plastic wrap and turn back corner to vent. Microwave at high (100%) power for $3\frac{1}{2}$ to $4\frac{1}{2}$ minutes or until fish is opaque and flakes easily with fork.

PER SERVING (using cod)	
calories	164
g fat	6
g protein	25
g carbohydrate	0
Excellent: niacin	

Quick and Easy Salmon Steaks with Watercress Sauce

Fresh salmon steaks are a wonderful treat and I like them best when simply cooked — either poached, steamed or microwaved, as long as they aren't overcooked. The easiest and fastest is the microwave. In summer, dress them up with this watercress sauce; in winter serve with the Fresh Dill Cream Sauce, page 137. (Recipe pictured opposite page 121.)

PER SERVING	
calories	295
g fat	11
g protein	43
g carbohydrate	3
Good: thiamin, calcium, iron	
Excellent: niacin	

4	salmon steaks, 1 in (2.5 cm) thick (5 oz [125 g] each)	
2 tsp	lemon juice	10 m
	freshly ground pepper	
	watercress sprigs	

Watercress Sauce

10 oz	low-fat cottage cheese	275
2½ oz	low-fat natural yogurt	60
1 oz	chopped fresh watercress leaves	25
2 tbsp	chopped fresh parsley	30 m
1 tbsp	chopped fresh chives	15 m
2 tsp	grated Parmesan cheese	10 m

Oven Steam Method
On lightly oiled large piece of foil, arrange salmon in single layer. Sprinkle with lemon juice, and pepper to taste. Fold foil over salmon and seal; place on baking sheet. Bake in 400°F (200°C) Gas Mark 6 oven for about 15 minutes or until fish is opaque and flakes easily with fork.

Microwave Method
In microwave-safe dish arrange salmon in single layer. Sprinkle with lemon juice, and pepper to taste. Cover with plastic wrap; fold back corner to vent. Microwave at high (100%) power for 5 minutes or until fish is opaque and flakes easily with fork.

The only way to ruin good-quality fish is to overcook it. If fillets or steaks are ¾ to 1 in (2–2.5 cm) thick, you'll be much less likely to overcook them than if they are thin. Cooking times in this recipe are based on 1 in (2.5 cm) thick steaks.

Watercress Sauce: In food processor, combine cottage cheese, yogurt, chopped watercress, parsley, chives and Parmesan; process until well mixed. Or pass cottage cheese through a sieve and combine with remaining ingredients.
Arrange salmon on plates and garnish with sprig of watercress. Pass sauce separately. Makes 4 servings.

Dilled Snapper Fillets with Cucumber and Yogurt Sauce

Any kind of fish fillets — salmon, sole, sea bass — can be used; just choose whatever is freshest. If at all possible, try to use fresh dill instead of dried because the flavour is quite different.

PER SERVING	
calories	127
g fat	3
g protein	21
g carbohydrate	3
Excellent: niacin	

4	red snapper fillets, about 1¼ lb (550 g)	4
1½ tsp	lemon juice	7 ml
1	clove garlic, crushed	1
2 tbsp	chopped fresh dill (or 1 tsp [5 ml] dried	30 ml

Cucumber and Yogurt Sauce

2½ oz	low-fat natural yogurt	60 g
2½ oz	light sour cream	60 g
2 oz	finely chopped or grated cucumber	50 g
1 tbsp	chopped spring onion	15 ml
	freshly ground pepper	

On grill pan or in microwave-safe dish, arrange fillets in single layer with thickest part to outside. Brush with lemon juice; sprinkle with garlic and dill. Grill for 6 to 8 minutes or microwave, covered loosely with waxed paper, at high (100%) power for 4 to 5 minutes or until fish is opaque and flakes easily when tested with fork.

Cucumber and Yogurt Sauce: Meanwhile, in small dish, combine yogurt, sour cream, cucumber, onion, and pepper to taste; mix well. Spread over fish and grill for 2 minutes or microwave at high (100%) power for 1 minute or until sauce is hot. Makes 4 servings.

Barbecued Skewered Halibut with Red Peppers and Mange Tout

These easy-to-make kebabs look festive, taste great and, as an added bonus, make the fish go further. Serve over rice along with Tomato Salsa Sauce (page 103) or Cucumber and Yogurt Sauce (page 97). Be sure to soak the wooden skewers in water for at least 30 minutes to prevent charring.

	SERVING	
calories		164
g fat		6
g protein		24
g carbohydrate		3
Good: fibre, iron		
Excellent: vitamin A, vitamin C, niacin		

1 lb	halibut or swordfish steaks	450 g
	juice of 1 lime	
1 tbsp	olive oil	15 ml
2 tbsp	chopped fresh coriander or parsley or dill	30 ml
	freshly ground pepper	
1	red pepper	1
20	mange tout	20

Cut fish into 1 in (2.5 cm) cubes; place in a single layer in a shallow dish. Sprinkle with lime juice, oil and coriander; cover and refrigerate for at least 30 minutes or up to 4 hours, turning once or twice.

Seed and cut red pepper into 1 in (2.5 cm) squares. String mange tout and blanch in boiling water for 1 minute or until bright green and easily bent.

Thread fish on water-soaked wooden skewers alternating with red pepper and mange tout folded in half. Cook over medium-hot grill or coals, turning once or twice, for 12 to 18 minutes or until fish is opaque. Makes 4 servings.

Linguine with Salmon and Chives

Tender-crisp cooked vegetables, such as asparagus, green peas or mushrooms, can be added to this quick and easy supper dish. Spring onions can be used instead of chives; cooked fresh salmon instead of canned.

PER SERVING	
calories	400
g fat	12
g protein	22
g carbohydrate	49
Good: calcium	
Excellent: niacin	

$\frac{1}{2}$ lb	linguine or any noodles	225 g
4 tsp	unsaturated margarine	20 ml
1	small onion, chopped	1
2 tbsp	plain, white flour	30 ml
8 fl oz	skimmed milk	250 ml
$\frac{1}{2}$ oz	chopped fresh chives	15 g
	freshly ground pepper	
1	tin (7.75 oz [220 g]) salmon	1
2 tbsp	grated Parmesan cheese	30 ml

Recipe includes juices from canned salmon. Although this adds to the fat content, these juices are an excellent source of omega 3 fatty acids, which current research indicates may help to reduce heart disease.

In large pot of boiling water, cook linguine until al dente (tender but firm); drain, reserving 2 fl oz (60 ml) cooking liquid. Return linguine to pan.

Meanwhile, in saucepan, melt margarine over medium heat; add onion and cook until tender. Stir in flour; mix well. Add milk and cook, whisking, until mixture comes to boil, thickens and loses any raw-flour taste. Stir in chives, pepper to taste, and add reserved cooking liquid.

Flake salmon and add along with juices and chive mixture to pot with linguine; mix lightly. Sprinkle Parmesan cheese over each serving. Makes 4 servings.

Tuscan-Style Spaghetti with Clams and Garlic

In Italy, this popular pasta dish is made with tiny tender clams that have about 1 in (2.5 cm) shells.

PER SERVING	
calories	293
g fat	7
g protein	10
g carbohydrate	46
Good: fibre, niacin	
Excellent: vitamin C, iron	

2 lb	small size clams (in shells)	1 kg
3	cloves garlic, crushed	3
2 tbsp	olive oil	30 m
2 fl oz	white wine	60 m
½ lb	capellini or spaghetti noodles	225 g
1 oz	chopped fresh parsley	25 g
	salt and freshly ground pepper	

Try to time cooking of pasta so it is ready the same time the clams are. If using dried pasta, start it before cooking clams; if using fresh or very fine pasta, cook clams first.

Scrub clams under cold running water: discard any that do not close when tapped.

In large heavy saucepan, cook garlic and oil over medium-high heat for 1 minute; add wine and clams. Cover and cook until clams open (time will vary from 2 to 10 minutes depending on size of clams); discard any that do not open. Meanwhile, in large pot of boiling water, cook spaghetti until al dente (tender but firm); drain.

Pour clam mixture over hot pasta and toss with parsley. Season with salt and pepper to taste. Makes 4 servings.

Fettuccine with Mussels, Leeks and Tomatoes

This gorgeous dish is perfect for a special little dinner. As well as being easy to make, it tastes and looks wonderful, too. Choose cultured mussels as they are easy to clean and have lots of meat inside.

3 lb	mussels	1.5 kg
2	leeks	2
$\frac{3}{4}$ lb	fettuccine	300 g
2 tbsp	olive oil	30 ml
4	cloves garlic, crushed	4
$\frac{1}{2}$ tsp	dried thyme	2 ml
4	tomatoes, coarsely chopped	4
$2\frac{1}{2}$ fl oz	dry white wine	75 ml
1 oz	coarsely chopped fresh parsley	25 g
	fresh ground pepper	

Scrub mussels under cold running water; cut off any hairy beards. Discard any that do not close when tapped.

Trim leeks, discarding dark green parts. Slice in half lengthwise and wash well. Cut into thin $1\frac{1}{2}$ in (4 cm) long strips and set aside.

In large pot of boiling water, cook fettuccine until al dente (tender but firm); drain and return to pot.

Meanwhile, in large heavy saucepan, heat oil over medium heat; cook garlic and thyme for 1 minute. Add mussels, leeks, tomatoes and wine; cover and bring to boil. Reduce heat and simmer for 5 to 8 minutes or until leeks are tender and mussels open (discard any that don't open).

Pour tomato mixture over fettuccine; add parsley, and pepper to taste. Toss to mix and serve on dinner plates or in large individual bowls. Makes 4 servings.

PER SERVING	
calories	540
g fat	10
g protein	29
g carbohydrate	82
Good: vitamin A, riboflavin, calcium	
Excellent: fibre, vitamin C, thiamin, niacin, iron	

Teriyaki Cod Fillets

These fillets are absolutely delicious when microwaved. Any kind of fish can be used in this recipe, but I like cod or salmon the best.

	PER SERVING	
calories		173
g fat		6
g protein		27
g carbohydrate		1
Excellent: niacin		

2 tbsp	dry sherry	30 ml
2 tbsp	water	30 ml
1 tbsp	soy sauce	15 ml
1 tbsp	vegetable oil	15 ml
2 tsp	grated root ginger	10 ml
1 tsp	granulated sugar	5 ml
1	clove garlic, crushed	1
1 lb	cod fillets, $\frac{3}{4}$ in (2 cm) thick	450 g

In shallow microwave-safe or conventional dish, combine sherry, water, soy sauce, oil, root ginger, sugar and garlic; stir to mix. Add fish fillets and arrange in single layer; marinate at room temperature for 20 minutes or refrigerate for up to 4 hours, turning once or twice.

Remove fillets from marinade and transfer marinade to small saucepan. Place fillets in single layer in steamer; cover and steam for 5 to 8 minutes or until fish is opaque and flakes easily when tested with fork. Meanwhile, heat marinade over low heat until warm; drizzle over fish before serving. Makes 4 servings.

Microwave Method
Cover dish (fish and marinade) and microwave at high (100%) power for 5 minutes or until fish is opaque and flakes easily when tested with fork.

Grilled Halibut Steaks with Tomato Salsa Sauce

As well as its delicious taste when barbecued, halibut is a good choice for grilling because it doesn't fall apart as some fish does. However, other kinds of firm-fleshed fish, such as salmon, can be substituted. Instead of a rich cream sauce, dress grilled fish with a light, fresh Mexican salsa. This fairly mild tomato and cucumber salsa does not overpower the delicate flavour of fish. For extra spiciness, add chopped hot peppers to taste.

PER SERVING	
calories	234
g fat	10
g protein	32
g carbohydrate	3
Good: vitamin C	
Excellent: vitamin A, niacin	

1½ lb	halibut steaks, about ¾ in (2 cm)thick	675 g
Tomato Salsa Sauce		
1½ oz	finely diced cucumber	40 g
1½ oz	finely diced red pepper	40 g
2 tbsp	finely diced red onion	30 ml
1	small ripe tomato, finely diced	1
2 tsp	red wine vinegar	10 ml
2 tsp	chopped fresh coriander (optional)	10 ml
½ tsp	Worcestershire sauce	2 ml
Dash	hot pepper sauce	Dash
1 tsp	olive oil	5 ml

Tomato Salsa Sauce: In bowl, combine cucumber, red pepper, onion, tomato, vinegar, coriander (if using), Worcestershire sauce, hot pepper sauce and oil; stir to mix. In food processor, purée half of the salsa mixture; combine with remaining salsa.

Grill fish, turning once, for about 4 minutes on each side or until fish is opaque and flakes easily when tested with fork. Place on serving platter or plates and spoon salsa over. Makes 4 servings.

Microwave Method
Place steaks in single layer in microwave-safe dish; cover and microwave at high (100%) power for 4 to 5 minutes or until opaque.

Swordfish Steaks with Lime and Coriander

Fresh lime juice and coriander complement the flavour of most fish. Swordfish is particularly good for barbecuing because its firm flesh doesn't fall apart. Other fresh fish steaks, such as halibut or salmon, are also delicious cooked this way. If fresh coriander isn't available, substitute other herbs, such as fresh parsley, dill, rosemary or oregano. Serve with Tomato Salsa Sauce (page 103). (Recipe pictured opposite page 153.)

1 lb	swordfish or halibut steaks (about ¾ in [2 cm] thick)	450
	juice of 1 lime	
1 tbsp	olive oil	15 m
2 tbsp	chopped fresh coriander (or ½ tsp [2 ml] ground)	30 m
	freshly ground pepper	
Garnish		
	lime wedges	
	fresh coriander sprigs	

Place fish in single layer in shallow dish. Sprinkle with lime juice, oil and coriander; cover and refrigerate for at least 15 minutes or up to 4 hours, turning once or twice.

Grill fish for 5 to 8 minutes or until fish is opaque and flakes easily when tested with fork. Turn halfway through. (Time will vary depending upon thickness of fish, about 10 minutes per 1 i [2.5 cm] of thickness.). Sprinkle with pepper to taste. Garnish each serving with lime wedges and sprigs of fresh coriander. Makes 4 servings.

PER SERVING	
calories	150
g fat	6
g protein	23
g carbohydrate	0
Excellent: vitamin A, niacin	

Fish Barbecue Dinner

Swordfish Steaks with Lime and Coriander (page 104)
Peas with Spring Onions (page 120)
New Potatoes with Herbs (page 132)
Peaches with Grand Marnier Sauce (page 161)

For other main-course dishes see lifestyle section, page 175.

MEATLESS MAIN COURSES

To make our diet more healthy we need to rely more on vegetable protein and less on animal protein. Legumes (beans, peas, lentils), nuts, seeds and grains can also provide protein, vitamins and minerals, and are higher in fibre and lower in saturated fat than animal protein.

Protein is made up of 22 amino acids. Nine of these amino acids can't be produced by the body and must be obtained from food. These are called essential amino acids. All animal products contain all the essential amino acids. Plant foods are missing an essential amino acid. Therefore, it is important to combine a plant food with an animal food or two plant foods that together contain all the essential amino acids. Good combinations of plant foods are:

   legumes and grains (e.g. baked beans and wholemeal bread)
   legumes and nuts (e.g. tossed salad with chick peas and walnuts)
   legumes and low-fat dairy products (e.g. bean casserole with low-fat mozzarella topping)
   grains and low-fat dairy products (e.g. cereal and skimmed milk)

When we serve a meatless meal, we can use some cheese and eggs and still keep our saturated fat content down to the recommended level. It's important to consider our diet over a day or week. It's when we eat meats, high-fat cheese and eggs on a daily basis that the fat will be too high. See other sections of this book for more meatless main-course dishes.

Bean Casserole with Tomatoes and Spinach

It seems that something that tastes as good as this should be harder to make. My son, Jeff, really likes this and says the Five-Grain Soda Bread (page 149) is perfect with it. Serve as a quick dinner or lunch along with a green salad. Sometimes I cook a pound (450 g) of minced beef along with the onions and add chilli powder.

PER SERVING	
calories	333
g fat	4
g protein	20
g carbohydrate	57

Good: thiamin, calcium
Excellent: fibre, vitamin A, vitamin C, niacin, iron

1 tbsp	unsaturated margarine or vegetable oil	15 ml
1	clove garlic, crushed	1
2	onions, sliced	2
1	can (14 oz [398 g]) tomatoes	1
1	can (19 oz [540 g]) red kidney beans, drained	1
1	can (19 oz [540 g]) pinto beans, drained	1
$\frac{1}{2}$ tsp	dried oregano	2 ml
1	pkg (10 oz [284 g]) fresh spinach (or 1 bunch) stems removed	1
	freshly ground pepper	

In large heavy saucepan or casserole, heat margarine over medium heat; cook garlic and onions, stirring occasionally, for 3 minutes or until softened.

Add tomatoes, breaking up with back of spoon. Add kidney and pinto beans, and oregano; bring to simmer.

Add spinach; cover and simmer until spinach is wilted, about 2 minutes. Season with pepper to taste. Makes 4 servings.

PER SERVING	
calories	304
g fat	14
g protein	16
g carbohydrate	31

Good: fibre, vitamin A, iron
Excellent: vitamin C, niacin,
calcium

Cheese

Cheese is a good source of
protein and calcium; however,
it (particularly Cheddar, Stilton
and Danish Blue) is high in fat.
If this is part of a meatless
meal, it can fit into a 30% fat
diet. If you are serving this
with meat, you should reduce
the cheese by half and use a
low-fat cheese such as low-fat
mozzarella or feta.

Barley, Green Pepper and Tomato Casserole

Serve this as a main course along with a tossed salad and wholemeal toast or pitta bread. Crumbled feta cheese is a nice addition.

8 oz	pot barley	225 g
1¼ pt	hot vegetable or chicken stock or water	750 ml
2	onions, chopped	2
1	green pepper, chopped	1
2	large tomatoes, cut in chunks	2
1 tsp	dried oregano	5 ml
	salt and freshly ground pepper	
8 oz	grated Cheddar cheese	225 g

In baking dish, combine barley, stock or water, onions, green pepper, tomatoes, oregano, and salt and pepper to taste; stir to mix. Cover and bake in 350°F (180°C) Gas Mark 4 oven for 45 minutes. Stir in cheese and bake, uncovered, for 25 minutes longer or until barley is tender and most liquid has been absorbed. Makes 6 servings.

The broccoli is added just before serving because the acid in the salad dressing will cause the broccoli to lose its bright green colour.

For other main-course salads see salad section (page 46).

For other main-course salads see salad section (page 46).

PER SERVING	
calories	229
g fat	13
g protein	9
g carbohydrate	20
Good: fibre, vitamin A, niacin, calcium	
Excellent: vitamin C	

*For any of the recipes in this book which suggest a low-fat mozzarella cheese, a low-fat cheddar cheese can be substituted if desired.

Tomato, Broccoli and Pasta Salad

This salad is perfect for buffets, with a green salad or soup for a main course. I like it with rigatoni, the large, tubular-shaped pasta, because it goes well with large chunks of tomato and broccoli; however, any other pasta can be substituted.

4 oz	rigatoni or other pasta	100 g
1 lb	broccoli florets	450 g
4 oz	chopped spring onions	100 g
3	tomatoes, cut in wedges	3
4 oz	low-fat mozzarella cheese, cubed*	100 g
½ oz	fresh parsley, finely chopped	15 g
Mustard Vinaigrette		
3 tbsp	lemon juice	45 ml
3 tbsp	water	45 ml
2	cloves garlic, crushed	2
1 tsp	Dijon mustard	5 ml
2 fl oz	vegetable oil	60 ml
	salt and freshly ground pepper	

In large pot of boiling water, cook pasta until al dente (tender but firm). Drain and rinse under cold water; drain again and set aside.

In another pot of boiling water, blanch broccoli for 2 minutes. Drain and rinse under cold water. Drain again and wrap in paper towel; set aside.

In salad bowl, combine pasta, green onions, tomatoes, cheese and parsley.

Mustard Vinaigrette: In food processor or mixing bowl, combine lemon juice, water, garlic, mustard and oil; mix well. Pour over salad and toss to mix. Add salt and pepper to taste.

Cover and refrigerate for 30 minutes or up to 4 hours. Just before serving, add broccoli and toss to mix. Makes 6 servings.

PER SERVING	
(meatless version)	
calories	368
g fat	11
g protein	14
g carbohydrate	55
Good: niacin, calcium, iron	
Excellent: fibre, vitamin A, vitamin C	

Adding chicken, turkey or
ham to this dish will increase
the protein. Adding ham will
also increase the salt.

Fusilli with Fresh Tomatoes, Basil and Parmesan

You can use any kind of pasta in this easy recipe. To preserve the fresh flavour and texture of the tomatoes they are quickly cooked over high heat. Once you have cooked the pasta, the whole mixture cooks in less than five minutes. (Recipe pictured opposite page 120).

½ lb	fusilli (corkscrew shape) or any tubular pasta	225 g
2 tbsp	vegetable oil or unsaturated margarine	30 ml
4	spring onions, chopped	4
4	tomatoes, coarsely chopped	4
3	cloves garlic, crushed	3
6 oz	strips or cubes cooked ham, turkey, chicken (optional)	150 g
1 oz	coarsely chopped fresh parsley	25 g
½ oz	coarsely chopped fresh basil (or 1 tsp [5 ml] dried)	15 g
2 oz	grated Parmesan cheese	50 g
	salt and pepper	

In large pot of boiling water, cook pasta until al dente (tender but firm); drain. (If sauce isn't ready, rinse pasta under warm water for a few seconds to prevent it sticking together.)

Meanwhile, in large heavy saucepan, heat oil over high heat. Add onions, tomatoes and garlic; cook, stirring, for 2 to 3 minutes or until tomatoes are just heated through but still hold their shape. Stir in rotini, ham (if using), parsley, basil and Parmesan. Reduce heat to medium; cook, stirring gently, for about 2 minutes or until heated through. Season with salt and pepper to taste. Makes 4 servings.

Easy July Supper

*Fettuccine with Pesto Sauce
(page 110)
Sliced Cucumbers with Chives
and Yogurt (omit Basil) (page
50)
Raw baby carrots
Wholemeal pitta bread
Strawberries with Orange and
Honey Yogurt (page 169)*

SERVING (MAIN COURSE)	
calories	542
g fat	12
g protein	20
g carbohydrate	88
Good: vitamin C, calcium, iron	
Excellent: fibre, niacin	

Freeze pesto sauce in ice-cube
containers; when frozen
transfer to plastic bag. Use a
cube to flavour soups, salad
dressing and sauces.

Fettuccine with Pesto Sauce

Pesto sauce is a fragrant fresh basil sauce that is absolutely
perfect over pasta. This version has a full, pungent basil flavour
yet omits the pine nuts and is much lower in oil than the classic
recipe.

1 lb	fettuccine	450
	freshly ground pepper	
	grated Parmesan cheese	

Pesto Sauce

2	cloves garlic	
1 oz	fresh basil leaves, lightly packed	25
2 oz	grated Parmesan cheese	50
2 tbsp	olive oil	30 m

In large pot of boiling water cook fettuccine until al dente
(tender but firm). While pasta is cooking, prepare sauce.

Pesto Sauce: In food processor, combine garlic and basil;
process until chopped. Add Parmesan and olive oil, process
until smooth. Remove 4 fl oz (125 ml) of the pasta cooking liquid
and add to sauce; process until smooth.

Drain pasta and toss with pesto sauce. Sprinkle with pepper
and Parmesan to taste. Makes 4 main course servings; 8 side
dish servings.

Compare	g fat per serving
This recipe	12
Most pesto sauce recipes	20 +

PER SERVING	
calories	332
g fat	11
g protein	22
g carbohydrate	37

Good: fibre, iron
Excellent: vitamin A, vitamin C,
niacin, calcium

How Much Pasta to Cook?

For a main course pasta dish which includes a number of ingredients along with pasta, I usually plan on about 1 lb (450 g) for 4 servings. If it is a dish with only a light sauce such as pesto with pasta I use more.

The easiest way to measure is to weigh the uncooked pasta. If you don't have scales you can estimate by dividing up the package according to total weight (i.e. divide a 1 lb [450 g] package in half to get lb [225 g]).

I usually try to cook more pasta than I need and use the extra to make a pasta salad or I mix it with any extra sauce and reheat it for breakfast or lunch.

Vegetable Lasagne

This is light and easy to make. It can be prepared a day or two in advance and refrigerated.

1 tbsp	vegetable oil	15 ml
1	small onion, chopped	1
3	cloves garlic, crushed	3
1	carrot, chopped	1
1	stick celery, chopped	1
6 oz	sliced mushrooms	150 g
1	can (19 oz [540 g]) tomatoes	1
3 tbsp	tomato purée	45 ml
6 tbsp	water	90 ml
1 tsp	each dried basil and oregano	5 ml
	salt and freshly ground pepper	
1 lb	small broccoli florets	450 g
9	lasagne sheets	9
10 oz	cottage cheese	250 g
12 oz	grated low-fat mozzarella cheese	300 g
1 oz	grated Parmesan cheese	25 g

In large saucepan, heat oil over medium heat; add onion and cook until tender. Stir in garlic, carrot, celery and mushrooms; cook, stirring often, for 5 minutes.

Add tomatoes, breaking up with fork. Stir in tomato sauce, basil, oregano; season with salt and pepper to taste. Simmer, uncovered, for 10 minutes or until thickened slightly. Let cool; stir in broccoli.

In large pot of boiling water, cook sheets until al dente (tender but firm); drain and rinse under cold water.

In lightly greased 13 × 9 in (3.5 lit) baking dish, arrange 3 sheets evenly over bottom. Spread with one-half of the vegetable mixture then half of the cottage cheese. Sprinkle with $\frac{1}{3}$ of the mozzarella cheese.

Repeat sheet, vegetable mixture, cottage and mozzarella cheese layers once. Arrange remaining sheets over top; sprinkle with remaining mozarella and Parmesan. Bake in 350°F (180°C) Gas Mark 4 oven for 35 to 45 minutes or until hot and bubbly. Makes 8 servings.

Cabbage and Potato Pie

Crinkly savoy cabbage, kale, or a combination of these in light cream sauce with mashed potato topping is a delicious vegetable dish.

PER SERVING	
calories	246
g fat	7
g protein	7
g carbohydrate	40
Good: vitamin A, thiamin, niacin, calcium	
Excellent: fibre, vitamin C	

1 lb	savoy cabbage and/or kale	450 g
4	medium potatoes, peeled and quartered	4
2 fl oz	skimmed milk	60 m
1 tbsp	unsaturated margarine	15 m
	freshly ground pepper	
	paprika	

Cream Sauce

1½ tbsp	unsaturated margarine	22 m
1	medium onion, chopped	1
2 tbsp	plain flour	30 m
8 fl oz	skimmed milk	250 m
	salt, freshly ground pepper and nutmeg	

Separate and trim cabbage leaves. In large pot of boiling water, cover and cook cabbage for 5 to 10 minutes, or until tender. Drain thoroughly; chop coarsely and set aside.

In saucepan of boiling water, cook potatoes until tender; drain. Mash potatoes along with milk, margarine and pepper to taste.

Cream Sauce: Meanwhile, in small saucepan, melt margarine over medium heat; add onion and cook for 3 to 5 minutes or until tender. Stir in flour and mix well; cook, stirring, for 1 minute. Add milk and cook, stirring, for 3 to 5 minutes or until mixture comes to simmer and has thickened. Season with salt, pepper and nutmeg to taste.

Mix sauce with cabbage; spoon into baking dish. Cover evenly with mashed potatoes; sprinkle lightly with paprika. Bake in 350°F (180°C) Gas Mark 4 oven for 20 to 30 minutes or until heated through. Makes 4 servings.

Winter Meatless Dinner

*Cabbage and Potato Pie
(page 112)
Baked Parsnips and Carrots
(page 118)
Wholemeal buns with low-fat
mozzarella cheese
Fresh-fruit compôte
Milk*

Gratin of Winter Vegetables

This cheese-topped vegetable casserole dish is a nice dish to serve as part of a meatless meal, or with roast chicken, turkey or meats.

2 tbsp	vegetable oil	30 ml
12 oz	thin strips of small yellow turnip	350 g
4 fl oz	water	125 ml
1	red pepper, cut in thin strips	1
4 oz	thinly sliced onion	100 g
12 oz	thinly sliced courgettes	300 g
3 oz	sliced mushrooms (about 8)	75 g
4	medium tomatoes, cut in chunks	4
½ tsp	dried oregano	2 ml
	salt and freshly ground pepper	
6 oz	grated low-fat mozzarella cheese	150 g
1 tbsp	grated Parmesan cheese	

In large pan, heat oil over medium heat. Add turnip and cover and cook for 10 minutes or until tender, stirring occasionally. If necessary, add more water to prevent burning. Add red pepper and onions; cook, stirring, for 2 minutes.

Add courgettes and mushrooms; cook, stirring, for 3 minutes. Add tomatoes and increase heat to high; cook, stirring occasionally, 5 to 10 minutes or just until excess moisture has evaporated. Stir in oregano; season with salt and pepper to taste.

Spoon vegetable mixture into shallow heatproof baking dish; sprinkle evenly with mozzarella and Parmesan cheeses. Grill for 3 to 5 minutes or until cheese is melted and slightly browned. Makes 8 servings.

PER SERVING	
calories	129
g fat	8
g protein	8
g carbohydrate	9

Good: fibre, vitamin A, niacin, calcium
Excellent: vitamin C

Recipe can be prepared in advance, covered and refrigerated. Reheat in 350°F (180°C) Gas Mark 4 oven for 20 to 25 minutes or microwave at high (100%) for 3 to 5 minutes or until heated through.

Mexican Rice and Bean Casserole

This is a well-liked dish at our house. You may want to add a little less chilli or cayenne if you have young children. Serve with a green vegetable, salad and toast.

	SERVING	
calories		268
g fat		5
g protein		14
g carbohydrate		45

Good: vitamin A, thiamin, calcium
Excellent: fibre, vitamin C, niacin, iron

1 tsp	vegetable oil	5 m
4 fl oz	water	125 m
1	onion, chopped	1
2	cloves garlic, crushed	2
4 oz	mushrooms, sliced	100 g
2	green peppers, chopped	2
5 oz	long-grain rice	125 g
1	can (28 oz [796 g]) red kidney beans, drained	1
1	can (19 oz [540 g]) tomatoes	1
1 tbsp	chilli powder	15 ml
2 tsp	cumin	10 ml
¼ tsp	cayenne pepper	1 ml
4 oz	grated low-fat mozzarella cheese	100 g

In large saucepan, heat oil with water over medium heat. Add onion, garlic, mushrooms and green peppers; simmer, stirring often, until onion is tender, about 10 minutes.

Add rice, beans, tomatoes, chilli powder, cumin and cayenne; cover and simmer for about 25 minutes or until rice is tender and most of the liquid is absorbed.

Transfer to baking dish and sprinkle with cheese. Bake in 350°F (180°C) Gas Mark 4 oven for 15 minutes or microwave at high (100%) power for 1 to 2 minutes or until cheese melts. Makes 6 servings.

VEGETABLES

When my daughter asks what's for dinner, she can't understand why I often answer by mentioning only the meat course; to her the vegetables are as important and most enjoyable. I, too, love vegetables but often plan meals around the meat or fish because they usually take more time to prepare or cook. For healthy eating, vegetables should cover at least three-quarters of your dinner plate.

Vegetables are an important source of vitamins, minerals, carbohydrates, protein and fibre, and are low in fats and calories.

Choose locally grown fresh vegetables that are in season for the best flavour and nutritive value. When out of season, frozen vegetables are often higher in nutritive value than fresh because imported vegetables lose nutrients during transportation and storage. For example, lettuce loses half its vitamin C in one week after it is picked. Canned vegetables are often higher in salt than fresh or frozen.

Compare Sodium Content

	Fresh	Canned	Frozen
Peas	5 mg	394 mg	147 mg
Green beans	4 mg	361 mg	19 mg

Cherry Tomatoes and Mushroom Sauté

This dish is good any time of year, but especially in the winter when cherry tomatoes are usually less expensive and have better colour and flavour than larger ones. Most fresh herbs can be used instead of dried.

PER SERVING	
calories	40
g fat	2
g protein	1
g carbohydrate	5
Good: fibre	
Excellent: vitamin C	

1 tbsp	unsaturated margarine	15 m
1	clove garlic, crushed	
$\frac{1}{2}$ lb	medium mushrooms, halved	225
12 oz	cherry tomatoes, stems removed	300
$\frac{1}{2}$ tsp	dried oregano (or 1 tbsp [15 ml] fresh)	2 m
$\frac{1}{2}$ tsp	dried thyme (or 1 tbsp [15 ml] fresh)	2 m
$\frac{1}{2}$ oz	chopped fresh parsley	12
	salt and freshly ground pepper	

In large nonstick pan, melt margarine over medium-high heat, cook garlic and mushrooms, shaking pan, for 3 minutes.

Add tomatoes, oregano and thyme; cook for 3 to 5 minutes or until tomatoes are heated through and mushrooms are tender.(Can be prepared an hour or two in advance and reheated.) Sprinkle with parsley; season with salt and pepper to taste. Makes 6 servings.

Chinese-Style Vegetables

Any seasonal vegetables can be added to this colourful stir-fry. Consider celery, onion, sweet peppers, mushrooms, green peas, beans, mange tout, tomatoes, asparagus or Brussels sprouts. Instead of red or green cabbage, consider using bok choy or Chinese lettuce.

1 tbsp	vegetable oil	15 ml
10 oz	cauliflower florets	275 g
10 oz	broccoli florets	275 g
4	medium carrots, sliced	4
4 fl oz	chicken stock	125 ml
$\frac{1}{4}$ lb	mange tout	100 g
1 tsp	garlic, chopped	5 ml
2 tbsp	fresh root ginger, chopped	30 ml
12 oz	chopped red or green cabbage or bok choy*	350 g
1 tsp	soy sauce	5 ml

In wok or large nonstick pan, heat oil over medium heat. Add cauliflower, broccoli and carrots; stir-fry for 3 minutes. Add chicken stock; cover and steam for 2 minutes.

Add mange tout; stir-fry for 1 minute. Add garlic, root ginger, and cabbage; stir-fry for 1 minute. Stir in soy sauce. Makes 6 servings.

*Bok choy is the Cantonese word for cabbage. We also call it Chinese cabbage. Its mild flavour is a pleasing addition to stir-fry, soup or salad. Chinese lettuce is a crinkly leafed lettuce also good in stir-frys.

PER SERVING	
calories	71
g fat	3
g protein	3
g carbohydrate	10

Excellent: fibre, vitamin A, vitamin C

Baked Parsnips and Carrots

As a child, parsnips were one of the few foods I didn't like; now I love them. I'm not sure if it was because of the parsnips themselves or that they might have been overcooked. In any case, parsnips cooked around a roast, baked or microwaved, are really sweet and delicious. Even my children like them this way.

PER SERVING	
calories	119
g fat	3
g protein	2
g carbohydrate	23
Good: vitamin C	
Excellent: fibre, vitamin A	

2	parsnips	
4	carrots	
1 tbsp	unsaturated margarine	15 m
	salt and freshly ground pepper	
Pinch	cumin (optional)	Pinc
1 tbsp	water	15 m

Peel parsnips and carrots; cut in half crosswise, then cut lengthwise into strips. Place in baking dish and dot with margarine. Sprinkle with salt, pepper and cumin (if using) to taste; add water.

Cover and bake in 375°F (190°C) Gas Mark 5 oven for 50 to 60 minutes or until vegetables are tender. Makes 4 servings.

Microwave Method
Prepare as above using a microwave-safe baking dish. Cover and microwave at high (100%) power for 12 to 15 minutes or until vegetables are tender.

roccoli is an excellent source f vitamin C and a good ource of Vitamin A and fibre.

PER SERVING	
calories	43
g fat	2
g protein	2
g carbohydrate	5
Good: fibre, vitamin A	
Excellent: vitamin C	

Make-Ahead Broccoli or Green Beans

you are entertaining, you might want to partially cook a green vegetable in advance. I nd this a big help when erving a first course at a inner party. It's hard to judge ow long it will take everyone eat the first course, let alone et to the table. If you put the roccoli on to cook before veryone sits down, it'll be vercooked. If you wait until fter the first course, it takes o long.

Cook prepared green egetable in boiling water until ender-crisp when pierced vith knife. Immediately drain nd plunge into large bowl of ce water. Drain and wrap in aper towels; refrigerate for up o 1 day.

To serve: Blanch vegetable n large pot of boiling water; rain thoroughly. Toss with nargarine and lemon juice or ther seasonings. **Note:** Don't dd lemon juice to a green egetable until just before erving. The acid will cause it o turn yellowish.

Broccoli with Ginger and Lemon

Fresh root ginger is delightful with broccoli; however, using garlic instead of ginger is equally good.

1	bunch broccoli (1¼ lb [550 g])	1
1 tbsp	vegetable oil or unsaturated margarine	15 ml
2 tsp	chopped fresh root ginger	10 ml
2 tbsp	lemon juice	30 ml
	freshly ground pepper	

Trim broccoli stalks (peel if tough) and cut into ½ in (1 cm) thick pieces. Separate top into florets. In large pot of boiling water, cook broccoli for 3 to 5 minutes or until tender-crisp when pierced with knife; drain.

Meanwhile, in small pan, heat oil or margarine over medium-low heat; cook root ginger for 2 minutes. Add lemon juice.

Transfer broccoli to warmed serving dish; pour lemon-juice mixture over. Sprinkle with pepper to taste and mix lightly. Makes 6 servings.

Courgettes with Chopped Tomatoes

In the summer and autumn when tomatoes are everywhere, thi is the way I often prepare courgettes.

1 tsp	unsaturated margarine	5 m
2	small onion, chopped	
4	small (6 in [15 cm]) courgettes, thinly sliced	
2	medium tomatoes, chopped	
	freshly ground pepper	

In a large nonstick pan, melt margarine over medium heat; add onions and cook, stirring, until softened. Add courgettes and cook for 2 minutes. Add tomatoes and cook for 3 to 5 minutes or until courgettes are tender-crisp. Season to taste wit pepper. Makes 4 servings.

PER SERVING	
calories	41
g fat	1
g protein	1
g carbohydrate	8
Good: fibre	
Excellent: vitamin C	

Peas with Spring Onions

Onions and green peas are a nice flavour combination. I use th white part of spring onions or chopped Spanish or normal cooking onions. Tiny pearl onions are lovely if you have the time it takes to peel them.

2 tsp	unsaturated margarine	10 m
4 oz	chopped onions (white parts) or Spanish or cooking onion	100
1 lb	frozen peas	450
	freshly ground pepper	

In nonstick pan, melt margarine over medium heat; add onions and cook, stirring often, until tender, about 5 minutes.
Meanwhile, blanch peas in boiling water; drain and add to pan. Sprinkle with pepper to taste and mix gently. Makes 6 servings.

PER 2 oz (50 g) SERVING	
calories	68
g fat	2
g protein	4
g carbohydrate	10
Good: vitamin A, fibre	
Excellent: vitamin C	

Right:
Fusilli with Fresh Tomatoes,
Basil and Parmesan (page 109)

PER SERVING	
calories	106
g fat	2
g protein	4
g carbohydrate	20

Good: fibre
Excellent: vitamin C

The Best Brussels Sprouts
When buying
Look for small, compact, firm,
bright-green Brussels sprouts.
Avoid ones with blemishes or
yellowing or a brownish or
slimy base.
When cooking
Prepare Brussels sprouts by
trimming outer leaves and
base. Cut shallow "X" in base
for even cooking. Boil, steam,
stir-fry or microwave, but
remember that it's very
important to cook for only a
short time — just until tender-
crisp. Overcooked Brussels
sprouts become strong-
flavoured and lose their bright-
green colour.

Left:
Quick and Easy Salmon Steaks
with Watercress Sauce
(page 96)

Brussels Sprouts with Peppers and Potatoes

Wonderful with turkey or roast chicken, this is a tasty, colourful vegetable dish to serve for Sunday dinner.

1 tbsp	unsaturated margarine or vegetable oil	15 ml
1	onion, chopped	1
1	large potato, cut in small cubes	1
1	bay leaf	1
1 lb	Brussels sprouts, halved if large	450 g
1	red pepper, cut in $\frac{1}{2}$ in (1 cm) pieces	1
2 fl oz	vegetable or chicken stock	60 ml
	freshly ground pepper	
2 tbsp	chopped fresh parsley or green onions	30 ml

In large nonstick pan, melt margarine over medium heat; cook onion, potato and bay leaf, stirring often, for 2 to 3 minutes or until onion is softened.

Add Brussels sprouts, red pepper and stock; cover and cook for 8 to 10 minutes or until sprouts and potatoes are tender (add water if necessary to prevent scorching).

Season with pepper to taste. Serve sprinkled with parsley. Makes 6 servings.

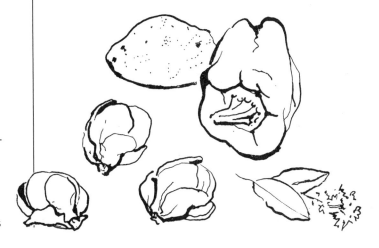

Green Beans with Sautéed Mushrooms

Mushrooms and herbs dress up green beans and add extra flavour. If you want to be really fancy, use wild mushrooms.

PER SERVING	
calories	57
g fat	3
g protein	2
g carbohydrate	6
Good: fibre, vitamin C	

¾ lb	green beans	350 g
1 tbsp	unsaturated margarine	15 m
1	clove garlic, crushed	
2 tsp	chopped fresh basil (or ½ tsp [2 ml] dried)	10 m
¼ tsp	dried crumbled rosemary	
8	medium mushrooms, sliced	
Dash	hot pepper sauce	Das

In saucepan of boiling water, cook beans for 6 to 8 minutes or until tender-crisp; drain.

Meanwhile in small saucepan or microwave-safe dish, melt margarine, add garlic, basil, rosemary, mushrooms and hot pepper sauce; cook over medium heat for 3 to 4 minutes, or cover and microwave at high (100%) power for 1 minute, or until mushrooms are tender.

Transfer beans to warm serving dish; pour mushroom mixture over and toss to mix. Makes 4 servings.

esh ginger is a fabulous
asoning for many vegetables
ch as in the Spring Greens
cipe presented here. Other
getables to stir-fry with
nger are broccoli, mange
ut, carrots or celery.

Spring Greens with Ginger and Celery

Kale, spring greens, spinach and cabbage are all delicious cooked this way, either on their own or in a combination. Some tougher greens should first be blanched. Rice vinegar is particularly good but any white vinegar can be used.

2 tbsp	cider, rice or white vinegar	30 ml
2 tbsp	water	30 ml
2 tsp	cornflour	10 ml
1 tsp	granulated sugar	5 ml
1 tbsp	vegetable oil	15 ml
1	onion, chopped	1
8 oz	sliced celery	225 g
12 oz	thinly sliced kale, spring greens, spinach or cabbage	350 g
1 tbsp	grated fresh root ginger	15 ml

In small dish, mix together vinegar, water, cornflour and sugar; set aside.

In large wok or nonstick pan, heat oil over medium-high heat. Add onion and stir-fry for 1 minute. Add celery, greens and root ginger; stir-fry for 1 minute. Add about 2 tbsp (30 ml) water; cover and steam for 3 minutes or until greens are wilted and celery is tender-crisp.

Pour in vinegar mixture and stir-fry for 1 minute or until liquid comes to boil. Serve immediately. Makes 5 servings.

Carrots and Leeks with Parsley

Choose tender, young carrots to combine with delicate-flavoured leeks. Chopped fresh dill, thyme or basil is a lovely addition to this dish.

PER SERVING	
calories	74
g fat	2
g protein	2
g carbohydrate	14
Good: vitamin C, fibre	
Excellent: vitamin A	

1 lb	carrots (6 medium)	450 g
4	medium leeks	4
2 tsp	water (for microwave method)	10 m
1 tbsp	unsaturated margarine	15 m
½ oz	chopped fresh parsley	15 g
	salt and freshly ground pepper	

To Clean Leeks

Trim base and tough green leaves from leeks, leaving tender green and white part.

If you want to use leeks whole, cut lengthwise in half part way down leek; otherwise cut in half lengthwise. Wash under cold running water, spreading leaves apart.

To Bake Leeks

Place leeks on lightly oiled foil, dot with a small amount of soft-polyunsaturated margarine and pepper. Wrap in foil. Bake in 350°F (180°C) Gas Mark 4 oven for 25 minutes or until tender.

Scrape carrots and cut diagonally into ¼ in (5 mm) thick slices. Clean leeks, discarding tough green parts. Slice white and tender green parts in half lengthwise; cut crosswise into ½ in (1 cm) thick slices.

Microwave Method

In microwave-safe dish, combine carrots and water; cover and microwave at high (100%) power for 5 minutes. Stir in leeks; dot with margarine. Cover and microwave at high (100%) power for 3 to 5 minutes or until vegetables are tender. Stir in parsley; season with salt and pepper to taste.

To steam

Place carrots in steamer over boiling water; cover and steam for 5 to 8 minutes or nearly tender-crisp. Add leeks and steam another 5 minutes. Transfer to warmed serving dish; toss with margarine, parsley, salt and pepper. Makes 6 servings.

Mushroom-Stuffed Courgettes

This is a delicious vegetable dish for a special dinner. It can be prepared early in the day then reheated in the oven or microwave just before serving.

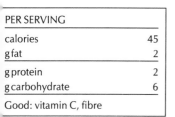

PER SERVING	
calories	45
g fat	2
g protein	2
g carbohydrate	6
Good: vitamin C, fibre	

2	medium courgettes (about 8–10 in [20–25 cm] in length)	2
2 tsp	unsaturated margarine	10 ml
3 oz	finely chopped mushrooms	75 g
1 tbsp	onion or shallots, finely chopped	15 ml
1 tbsp	fresh parsley, finely chopped	15 ml
	salt and freshly ground pepper	
1 tbsp	grated Parmesan cheese	15 ml

Trim ends from courgettes; cut crosswise into 1 in (2.5 cm) thick pieces. Steam courgettes for about 5 minutes or until tender-crisp; let cool. Scoop out small hollow from one end of each piece; set aside.

In nonstick pan, melt margarine over medium-high heat; cook mushrooms and onion or shallots, stirring, for 2 minutes or until onion is tender. Stir in parsley; season with salt and pepper to taste. Spoon mushroom mixture into courgette cavities. Arrange in microwave-safe dish or baking dish. Sprinkle with Parmesan cheese.

Just before serving, microwave at high (100%) power for 1 to 2 minutes or bake in 350°F (180°C) Gas Mark 4 oven for 15 to 20 minutes or until heated through. Makes 4 servings.

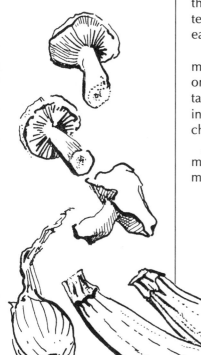

Low-Fat Cooking Tip
In many recipes vegetables are cooked in margarine or oil to soften and develop flavour. It's important to use as little fat as possible.

If vegetables stick to the pan, or to prevent scorching, add water a spoonful at a time and cook until water evaporates.

PER SERVING	
calories	107
g fat	7
g protein	2
g carbohydrate	11
Good: fibre, niacin	
Excellent: vitamin C	

Stir-Fry Ratatouille

This version of the colourful Mediterranean vegetable dish is lower in oil and quicker to make than most and is good hot or cold. It's a colourful autumn dish to serve with rice and cold meat or grilled lamb chops; for a meatless meal, cover with grated cheese and place under grill until cheese melts and is golden brown.

2 tbsp	vegetable oil	30 m
1	medium onion, sliced	
2	cloves garlic, crushed	
8	medium mushrooms, halved	
1	small yellow or red pepper, cubed	
12 oz	cubed ($\frac{1}{2}$ in [1 cm] pieces) unpeeled aubergine	350
1	small courgettes, sliced	
2	tomatoes, cut in wedges	
$\frac{1}{2}$ tsp	each dried thyme and basil	2 m
	salt and freshly ground pepper	

In large nonstick pan, heat half of oil over medium-high heat; add onion, garlic, mushroom and pepper and stir-fry until tender, about 4 minutes. With slotted spoon remove to side dish and set aside.

Heat remaining oil in pan; add aubergine, courgettes; stir-fry for 4 minutes or until tender. Return mushroom mixture to pan; add tomatoes, thyme, basil; cover and simmer for 5 minutes. Add salt and pepper to taste. Makes 6 servings.

Middle-Eastern Aubergine Baked with Yogurt and Fresh Mint

This is one of the tastiest and easiest ways to prepare aubergine. It's very good with lamb. You can also serve it with pork, beef or chicken or as part of a buffet or meatless dinner.

3 tbsp	vegetable oil	45 ml
2 tbsp	water	30 ml
1	large onion, sliced	1
1	medium aubergine, unpeeled (1$\frac{1}{4}$ lb [550 g])	1
9 oz	low-fat natural yogurt	230 g
3 tbsp	chopped fresh mint and/or parsley	45 ml
2	cloves garlic, crushed	2
	salt	
	freshly ground pepper	
	paprika	

In large nonstick pan, heat 1 tsp (5 ml) of the oil and water over medium heat; cook onion, stirring, for 5 minutes or until softened. Remove onion and set aside.

Cut aubergine into $\frac{1}{4}$ in (5 mm) thick slices. Brush remaining oil over aubergine slices. In pan over medium heat, cook aubergine (in batches) turning once, until tender, about 10 minutes (or arrange in a single layer on baking sheet and bake in 400°F [200°C] Gas Mark 6 oven for 15 minutes or until tender and soft).

In ungreased shallow baking dish, arrange overlapping slices of aubergine alternating with onion.

In small bowl, stir together yogurt, fresh mint or parsley, garlic, salt, and pepper to taste; drizzle over aubergine slices. Sprinkle liberally with paprika. Bake in 350°F (180°C) Gas Mark 4 oven until hot and bubbly, 10 to 15 minutes. Makes 6 servings.

PER SERVING

calories	116
g fat	7
g protein	3
g carbohydrate	10
Good: fibre	

Variation
When tomatoes are in season, add slices of tomato between aubergine slices and onion in baking dish. Sprinkle top with grated low-fat mozzarella or cheddar cheese.

PER SERVING	
calories	121
g fat	3
g protein	3
g carbohydrate	22
Good: niacin	
Excellent: fibre, vitamin A, vitamin C	

Steamed Fresh Vegetables

It's easy to add interest and flavour to a dinner by serving a combination of four colourful vegetables. It takes the same amount of time to peel two carrots and two parsnips as it does to peel four carrots. It's also a great way to use up the four mushrooms or half a stalk of broccoli lurking in the back of your refrigerator. Other vegetables to substitute or add: celery, fennel, sweet red or green pepper, mange tout, cauliflower, courgettes, cabbage and Brussels sprouts.

2	medium carrots, peeled and sliced	
2	medium parsnips, peeled and sliced	
1	stalk broccoli, cut in florets	
8	mushrooms	
1 tbsp	unsaturated margarine	15 m
	salt and freshly ground pepper	

Steam carrots and parsnips for 3 to 5 minutes or until tender-crisp. Add broccoli and mushrooms; steam for 3 minutes or until broccoli is bright green. Transfer to warm serving dish and add margarine. Sprinkle lightly with salt and pepper to taste; toss to mix.

Microwave Method
In microwave-safe dish, combine carrots, parsnips, broccoli and mushrooms. Add 1 tbsp (15 ml) water. Dot with margarine; sprinkle with pepper to taste. Cover with lid; microwave at high (100%) power for 6 minutes or until vegetables are tender; rotate dish once or twice during cooking. Add salt to taste. Makes 4 servings.

Steamed Fennel with Courgette and Spring Onions
The mild liquorice flavour of fennel makes a pleasing addition to courgettes and carrots.

Cut about 6 spring onions in half lengthwise then cut into 2 in (5 cm) lengths. Steam onions, and 10 oz (250 g) each julienne (thin strips) carrots, fennel, and courgettes for 6 to 8 minutes or until tender-crisp.

Transfer to warm serving platter and toss with a small amount of margarine, salt and freshly ground pepper to taste. Makes 6 servings.

Turnip and Apple Purée

Apple adds a mellow, sweet flavour to yellow turnip. For an equally delicious variation, use pear instead of apple. The recipe can be prepared up to a day in advance, but omit the yogurt and add when reheating.

1	small turnip (about 1¼ lb [550 g]) peeled and cubed	1
1	large apple, peeled, cored and cut in chunks	1
2½ oz	low-fat natural yogurt	60 g
1 tbsp	unsaturated margarine	15 ml
Pinch	nutmeg	Pinch
	salt and freshly ground pepper	

Steam turnip for 15 to 20 minutes or until nearly tender. Add apple and cook for 5 to 10 minutes or until turnip and apple are tender. Drain well.

In food processor or blender, purée turnip mixture until smooth. Add yogurt, margarine and nutmeg; season with salt and pepper to taste and process just until combined. Reheat in saucepan over medium-low heat or in microwave until heated through. Makes 6 servings.

PER SERVING	
calories	54
g fat	2
g protein	1
g carbohydrate	9
Good: fibre, vitamin C	

Light Dinner

Fettucine with Pesto Sauce (page 110)
Baked Tomatoes with Goat Cheese and Basil (page 130)
Wholemeal and Oatmeal Bread (page 150)
Strawberries with almonds and Amaretto

A soft or cream goat cheese, or chèvre, has a distinctive flavour that is lovely with tomatoes. If not available, use fresh mozzarella instead

PER SERVING	
calories	58
g fat	3
g protein	3
g carbohydrate	5
Good: fibre, vitamin A	
Excellent: vitamin C	

Baked Tomatoes with Goat Cheese and Basil

This simple dish is one of my favourites for entertaining. It goes well with any meat or poultry or as part of a buffet or meatless meal. It tastes best when made in the late summer when tomatoes are juicy and full of flavour.

4	medium tomatoes	4
3 oz	soft goat cheese (chèvre)	75 g
	freshly ground pepper	
3 tbsp	chopped fresh basil	45 m

Slice each tomato into about 4 thick slices. Arrange in single layer in shallow baking dish or microwave-safe dish.

Thinly slice goat cheese; arrange over tomatoes. Sprinkle with pepper to taste, then basil. Grill for 2 to 3 minutes or microwave at high (100%) power for 2 minutes or until cheese melts. Makes 6 servings.

Fettuccine with Basil and Parsley

Serve this as a side dish with any meats or as part of a meatless meal. Keep a pot of fresh parsley on the windowsill or a bunch in a plastic bag in the refrigerator to give a fresh flavour to this dish. Use any other fresh herbs you have, such as sage, rosemary or thyme (start with 1 tbsp [15 ml] and add more to taste), before adding dried.

4 oz	fettuccine or any pasta	100 g
1 tbsp	unsaturated margarine	15 ml
1	clove garlic, crushed	1
$\frac{1}{2}$ oz	chopped fresh parsley	15 g
$\frac{1}{2}$ oz	chopped fresh basil (or 1 tsp [5 ml] dried)	15 g
	freshly ground pepper	

In large pot of boiling water, cook noodles according to package directions or until al dente (tender but firm). Drain in colander.

Add margarine and garlic to pot; cook, stirring, for 1 minute over medium heat. Add hot noodles, parsley, basil, and pepper to taste; toss to mix. Serve hot. Makes 4 servings.

PER SERVING	
calories	237
g fat	4
g protein	7
g carbohydrate	43
Good: fibre	

Variation

Add one large tomato, chopped, along with herbs. Sprinkle each serving with grated Parmesan cheese. Make capellini or vermicelli noodles and serve as a first course.

Starchy foods or complex carbohydrates, such as wholemeal breads, pastas, rice, potatoes, are not high in fat or calories. They are a good source of B vitamins, iron and trace minerals. It's what we add to these starchy foods that increases the fat content in our diet.

Compare	Per tbsp (15 ml)	
Baked potato toppings	g fat	calories
Yogurt	1 or less	2 or less
Sour cream (low fat)	3	28
Butter or margarine	11	100

Bulgur, or cracked wheat, is available in some supermarkets and most health food stores. It is a good source of fibre.

PER SERVING	
calories	230
g fat	3
g protein	8
g carbohydrate	44
Good: iron	
Excellent: niacin, fibre	

Garlic and Parsley Potatoes
Boil 1 lb (450 g) tiny new potatoes, red-skinned potatoes or any you have on hand until tender. Peel only if skins are old and tough, because the skins add flavour, fibre and vitamins.

In small saucepan or microwave dish combine 2 tsp (10 ml) margarine or oil and 2 cloves crushed garlic and cook over medium heat, stirring, for 1 minute or microwave on medium (50%) power for 30 seconds.

Drain potatoes and cut in half or quarters if large; transfer to warm serving dish. Toss with garlic mixture and ⅓ oz (10 g) chopped fresh parsley. Makes 4 servings.

Variation
Instead of potatoes use green beans, carrots, cauliflower, broccoli or peas.

PER SERVING (including oil)	
calories	109
g fat	1
g protein	2
g carbohydrate	23
Excellent: vitamin C	

Bulgur Pilaf with Apricots and Raisins

Bulgur is the rice of the Mediterranean. Its mild nutty flavour and slightly crunchy texture are a nice change from rice.

2 tsp	unsaturated margarine	10 ml
1	onion, chopped	1
6 oz	bulgur or cracked wheat	150 g
2 oz	raisins	50 g
1½ oz	diced dried apricot	40 g
16 fl oz	boiling chicken stock	500 ml
½ oz	chopped fresh parsley (optional)	15 g
	salt and freshly ground pepper	

In nonstick pan, melt margarine over medium heat; cook onion, stirring, until softened. Stir in bulgur and cook, stirring, for 1 minute. Stir in raisins, apricot and stock; cover and simmer over low heat for 15 minutes or until liquid is absorbed. Stir in parsley (if using); season with salt and pepper to taste. Makes 4 servings.

New Potatoes with Herbs

Small new potatoes, boiled in their skins, are delicious. Instead of butter, top with chopped fresh herbs and a dash of lemon juice and oil. These go well with any meats, poultry or fish.

1 lb	tiny new potatoes (about 20)	450 g
1 tbsp	chopped fresh basil or thyme	15 ml
1 tbsp	chopped chives	15 ml
1 tsp	lemon juice	5 ml
1 tsp	olive or vegetable oil (optional)	5 ml
	freshly ground pepper	

In a saucepan, boil unpeeled potatoes until tender, about 15 minutes; drain. Add basil, chives, lemon juice, oil, and pepper to taste. Mix lightly and serve. Makes 4 servings.

Types of Lentils

Split red lentils are used in most soups and cook in 10 to 15 minutes.

Green or brown whole lentils retain their shape when cooked and take about 45 minutes to cook.

PER SERVING	
calories	144
g fat	3
g protein	8
g carbohydrate	23
Good: vitamin C, iron	
Excellent: fibre	

How to Cook Dried Lentils

Lentils are a good source of iron and an excellent source of fibre and vegetable protein. Serve with complementary cereal protein such as bread or rice. Uncooked dried lentils will yield twice their volume when cooked.

Wash and drain dried lentils. In saucepan, combine lentils with 3 times the amount of water (add a quartered onion and bay leaf if desired). Bring to a boil; reduce heat and simmer covered for 10 to 45 minutes depending on type, or until tender; drain. Use in salads, casseroles, soups or as a vegetable.

Quick Lentils with Onion and Celery

Keep a can of cooked lentils or a packet of dried red lentils on your shelf and you can have a quick vegetable dish in minutes.

1 tbsp	unsaturated margarine or vegetable oil	15 ml
2	onions, chopped	2
2	sticks celery, chopped	2
1	clove garlic, crushed	1
1	can (19 oz [540 g]) lentils, drained	1
Pinch	dried oregano	Pinch
	salt and freshly ground pepper	
1 oz	chopped fresh parsley	25 g

In pan, heat margarine over medium-high heat; cook onions, celery and garlic, stirring, for 3 minutes or until onion is tender. Add lentils and oregano; cook until heated through. Season with salt and pepper to taste; sprinkle with parsley. Makes 4 servings.

Dish can be prepared a day in advance and refrigerated. Reheat, covered, in 350°F (180°C) Gas Mark 4 oven for 30 minutes.

Pot or Pearl Barley?
What's the difference? Pearl is more polished than pot barley. When possible, choose pot barley because it is higher in fibre and more nutritious. They take the same length of time to cook. Use as an alternative to rice or pasta, in soups and casseroles.

PER SERVING	
calories	122
g fat	2
g protein	5
g carbohydrate	21
Good: fibre	
Excellent: niacin	

Variation
Rice and Mushroom Pilaf
Substitute 10 oz (250 g) long grain rice or brown rice for the barley. Stir rice into mushroom mixture. Reduce cooking time to about 40 minutes or until liquid has been absorbed.

The British Heart Foundation recommends that we reduce the fat, particularly saturated fat, in our diet and increase the complex carbohydrate. One way to do this is to have more rice, pasta or grains.

Barley and Mushroom Pilaf

I like to serve this as an alternative to rice or potatoes. Sometimes I vary it by adding chopped almonds, chopped celery or spring onion, chopped fresh dill, thyme or basil. It's nice for a buffet and can be prepared in advance.

1 tbsp	unsaturated margarine	15 m
1	onion, chopped	
$\frac{3}{4}$ lb	mushrooms, sliced	350
8 oz	pot barley	225
$1\frac{1}{4}$ pt	hot chicken stock	750 m
$\frac{2}{3}$ oz	chopped fresh parsley	20
	freshly ground pepper	

In nonstick pan, melt margarine over medium heat; add onion and cook for about 2 minutes or until softened. Add mushroom and cook, stirring occasionally, for 5 minutes.

Transfer mixture to 11 × 7 in (2 lit) baking dish; add barley and chicken stock. Bake, covered, in 350°F [180°C] Gas Mark 4 oven for 1 hour; uncover and bake for 10 minutes longer (or bake in 325°F [160°C] Gas Mark 3 oven for $1\frac{1}{2}$ hours). Stir in parsley and pepper to taste. Makes 8 servings.

ompare	Per 6 oz (150 ml) cooked				
	g fat	g fibre	g protein	g carbohydrate	calories
ulgur, or cracked wheat	1	4	6	41	191
ice, white	0	0.6	4	50	223
ice, brown	1	2	5	50	232
Macaroni	0.5	1	5	31	150
paghetti	0.5	1	5	31	150

inds of Rice
White rice is most common
n Britain; during
rocessing the bran is
emoved.

rown rice is the most
utritious because it
ontains the bran and
erm. It's higher in fibre
nd B vitamins than other
ce.

Wild rice is not really a rice
but we use it as a rice. It has
a wonderful nutty flavour
and chewy texture. It is
expensive and is often
served mixed with cooked
white or brown rice.
To cook: Rinse under
running water. Place in a
saucepan. For each 6 oz
(150 g) of rice add 2 pt (1 lit)
cold water; bring to a boil.
Cover and boil for 40
minutes or until grains are
firm-tender but not mushy
or splayed; drain.

Short- or long-grain rice
Short-grain cooked rice is
more sticky. The long-grain
rice is more firm and
separate after cooking.

To Cook Rice
Rinse under cold water. For
each 6 oz (150 g) of rice
bring 1 pt (540 ml) of water
or stock to a boil. Stir in
rice; reduce heat, cover
and simmer for 20+
minutes for white, 45
minutes for brown or until
water is absorbed and rice
is tender. 6 oz (150 g) of
uncooked rice yields about
18 oz (450 g) when cooked.

Fresh Tomato Sauce

One of my favourite meals in August and September is a fresh tomato sauce made with plum tomatoes and fresh herbs served over pasta. Sometimes I add some cooked Italian sausage. I don't follow a recipe and the result is slightly different every time.

Cook a few pounds of small plum tomatoes (chopped) in a spoonful or two of olive oil (sometimes I add a chopped onion and garlic) until they are soft, nearly smooth, thick and of a saucelike consistency. This should take about 30 minutes. Add a handful of chopped fresh basil, or a pinch of dried rosemary or oregano, and you will have a wonderful Italian tomato sauce to toss with pasta. Top with freshly grated Parmesan cheese.

Is it necessary to peel and seed tomatoes?

The skin and seeds of tomatoes are high in fibre. I only peel tomatoes if the skin is very tough. When making a sauce using the small plum tomatoes, peeling isn't necessary.

The easiest way to peel tomatoes it to put them in a pot or bowl and cover with boiling water; let stand for about 30 seconds, then drain. The skin can easily be removed using a knife.

SAUCES AND ACCOMPANIMENTS

Sauces are like jewellery: they add the finishing touch to a meal can dress it up and pull it all together. Many traditional sauces contain large amounts of saturated fat and calories from the butter, cream and eggs used.

To Reduce Fat in Sauces

- Use skimmed milk not whole milk.
- Use yogurt or milk instead of cream.
- Use half cream or single cream instead of double cream, or better still use milk.
- Use fromage frais instead of a roux.
- Use recommended oil or margarine instead of butter and use as little as possible.
- Use low-fat cheese instead of high-fat cheese.
- Use flour or cornflour to thicken instead of egg yolk.
- Use thinner sauces or reduced sauces instead of thick sauces.
- Use meat drippings (au jus) instead of fatty gravies.
- Use a different kind of sauce (cranberry sauce, apple sauce or a relish) instead of gravy.
- Use the sauce recipes in this book.

f serving as part of a meatless meal, you could add a little extra low-fat cheese for more protein.

PER 4 tbsp (60 ml) SERVING	
calories	97
g fat	6
g protein	6
g carbohydrate	4
Good: Calcium	

Fresh Dill Cream Sauce
Prepare cheese sauce recipe omitting grated cheese. Instead add ⅓ oz (10 g) (not packed) chopped fresh dill, ¼ tsp (1 ml) salt, ¼ tsp (1 ml) dried mustard, and freshly ground pepper to taste. Serve with salmon, sole or other fish either whole or in fillets or steaks. It's also very good with cauliflower.
    Fresh dill makes this sauce delicious. If unavailable, use ⅓ oz (10 g) chopped fresh parsley and 1 tsp (5 ml) dried dill. Other fresh herbs such as basil are also good but the amounts will vary. Add a tablespoon at a time and taste.

Cream Sauce
Prepare cheese sauce recipe, omitting grated cheese

Cheese Sauce

Cheese sauce is a traditional favourite to serve over cauliflower, broccoli, or other steamed vegetables and pasta. Because it adds extra fat but is a source of protein, it's a good choice to serve with a meatless meal. Using skimmed milk and a low-fat cheese keeps the saturated fat content at a minimum.

1½ tbsp	unsaturated margarine	22 ml
2 tbsp	plain flour	30 ml
8 fl oz	skimmed milk	250 ml
4 oz	grated low-fat mozzarella cheese	100 g
	cayenne pepper	

In saucepan, melt margarine over medium-low heat. Stir in flour and mix well; cook for 1 minute.
    Stir in milk and cook over medium heat, stirring, 3 to 5 minutes, until mixture comes to a low boil and has thickened. Add cheese and stir until melted. Season with cayenne to taste. Makes approximately 12 fl oz (375 ml).

Compare	per 4 tbsp (60 ml) serving	
Cheese sauce made with:	g fat	calories
Skimmed milk and low-fat cheese	6	97
Semi-skimmed milk and low-fat cheese	7	103
Whole milk and Cheddar cheese	10	134

To serve with fish or seafood, substitute dill for tarragon. To serve with lamb or chicken, you could substitute basil for tarragon.

1 tbsp (15 ml) SERVING	
calories	26
g fat	1
g protein	2
g carbohydrate	2

Herb Shaker

Here is a great suggestion for reducing your intake of salt. Instead of salt keep a mixture of herbs handy and use to season meats, poultry, soups, salads or salad dressings.

One pleasing combination is 1 tsp (5 ml) each of dried thyme, sage and rosemary mixed with 1½ tsp (7 ml) of dried marjoram.

Yogurt Béarnaise Sauce

In this version of a Béarnaise sauce, the classic accompaniment to steak, I use Greek yogurt instead of butter and half the usual number of egg yolks — so I call it a halfway healthy sauce. It's delicious with grilled chicken, turkey, lamb or fish.

4 tsp	chopped shallots or onions	20 m
2 fl oz	white wine	60 m
1	small clove garlic, crushed	1
1 tbsp	chopped fresh tarragon (or 1¼ tsp [6 ml] dried)	15 m
9 oz	Greek yogurt	230 g
2	egg yolks	2
1 tsp	cornflour	5 m
¼ tsp	granulated sugar	1 m
	salt, cayenne and freshly ground pepper	

In small saucepan, combine shallots, wine, garlic and tarragon; bring to boil over medium heat. Boil until liquid is reduced to 1 tbsp (15 ml).

In top of nonaluminium double boiler or saucepan, beat together yogurt, egg yolks, cornflour and sugar; add wine mixture.

Cook over simmering water, stirring often, until sauce has thickened, about 20 minutes. Remove from heat and season to taste with salt, cayenne and pepper. Serve warm.

Sauce can be prepared in advance and refrigerated for up to 1 week. Reheat over hot water or at low (10%) power in microwave. Makes enough for 12 people.

Compare: per tbsp (15 ml)	g fat	calories
This recipe	1	26
Normal Béarnaise sauce	12	117

PER 2 fl oz (60 ml) SERVING

calories	11
g fat	0
g protein	0
g carbohydrate	3

Cooking Beetroots
Beetroots can be steamed, baked or microwaved as well as boiled. Don't peel before cooking beetroots for they will ''bleed'' too much. Boiling and steaming take about the same time. Baking takes longer. Large old beetroots take twice as long to cook as young ones.

To microwave 1½ lb (675 g) medium to small beetroots: Place in microwave-safe dish; add 2 fl oz (60 ml) water. Cover with lid or vented plastic wrap and microwave on high 100%) power for 12 to 15 minutes or until tender.

Beetroot Vinaigrette
Slice or julienne 1½ lb (675 g) cold cooked beetroots and toss with Mustard and Garlic Vinaigrette (page 62). Makes 6 servings. Add chopped onions, chives or parsley. A beautiful addition to main meal or appetizer salads. Use in late-summer menus.

Old-Fashioned Pickled Beetroots

These are extremely easy to make, especially if you have any leftover cooked beetroot. They are a colourful addition to appetizer trays, salads, buffets and potluck dinners and are good with hot or cold meats.

9	medium beetroots (or 1½ lb [675 g] trimmed baby beets)	9
8 fl oz	water	250 ml
8 fl oz	cider or white vinegar	250 ml
3 tbsp	granulated sugar	45 ml

Trim beetroots leaving at least 1 in (2.5 cm) stems attached. Place in saucepan and cover with warm water; bring to boil and simmer for 40 minutes or until tender.

Drain and rinse under cold running water. Using fingers, slip off skins. Quarter or cut into thick slices and place in clean 40 fl oz (1 lit) jar.

In saucepan, combine water, vinegar and sugar; heat until sugar dissolves. Pour over beetroots; cover and let cool. Refrigerate for up to 1 month.

Compare: The British Heart Foundation recommends we limit our sodium intake to 3000 mg per day. Pickles, especially dill pickles, can be very high in sodium; instead choose homemade pickled beets.

	mg sodium
Pickled beets 4 tbsp (60 ml)	16
Dill pickle, 1 (4 in [10 cm])	1942

Cucumber Relish

This recipe from my friend Evelyn Barrigar makes the best relish I've ever tasted. Serve it with cold meats, chops or hamburgers.

1 tbsp (15 ml) SERVING	
calories	19
g fat	0
g protein	0
g carbohydrate	5

1 lb 6 oz	coarsely shredded peeled cucumbers*	600 g
10 oz	chopped onions	250 g
1	red pepper, chopped	
half	bunch celery, chopped	hal
1 lb	brown sugar	450 g
$1\frac{1}{2}$ tsp	salt	7 m
20 fl oz	white vinegar	600 m
6 tbsp	plain flour	90 m
$\frac{1}{2}$ tsp	ground turmeric	2 m
$\frac{1}{2}$ tsp	dry mustard	2 m

In large heavy saucepan, combine cucumbers, onions, red pepper, celery, sugar, salt and 15 fl oz (450 ml) of the vinegar. Bring to boil over medium-high heat and boil for 15 minutes.

Meanwhile, in small bowl, blend together flour, turmeric, mustard and remaining vinegar until smooth; whisk into cucumber mixture. Boil for 15 minutes (reduce heat but maintain a boil), stirring and skimming off any foam. Be careful mixture doesn't burn.

Ladle into sterilized jars, leaving $\frac{1}{4}$ in (5 mm) headspace. Immediately cover with sterilized lids and seal tightly. Makes about 80 fl oz (2 lit).

*About $3\frac{1}{2}$ large cucumbers. If cucumbers have large seeds, remove and discard before shredding.

Red Pepper Jelly

One year I make this with red peppers, the next, I use green. It is extremely quick and easy to make, is delicious with roast pork or chicken and is a nice small gift for friends.

2 lb	granulated sugar	900 g
10 oz	finely chopped or puréed red or green peppers (3 medium peppers)	250 g
12 fl oz	white vinegar	375 ml
1	bottle (170 ml) liquid pectin	1

In large saucepan, combine sugar, red peppers and vinegar; stir and bring to full boil. Boil over medium heat for 15 minutes, skimming off foam. Remove from heat; blend in pectin and stir for 2 minutes.

Pour into sterilized jars, leaving $\frac{1}{4}$ in (5 mm) headspace; seal with paraffin wax (see page 143). Cover with lids. Store in cool, dry place. Makes about $2\frac{1}{2}$ pt (1.5 lit).

PER 1 tbsp (15 ml) SERVING

calories   40
g fat   0

g protein   0
g carbohydrate   10

Use this relish and jelly instead of gravy and rich sauces.

Fresh Mint Sauce

Make this accompaniment to roast lamb in the summer when fresh mint is everywhere because it grows like a weed. Since I'm a lazy gardener, I just keep a pot of it near the back door.

3 tbsp	granulated sugar	45 ml
$2\frac{1}{2}$ fl oz	cider vinegar	75 ml
2 fl oz	water	60 ml
$1\frac{1}{2}$ tsp	cornflour	7 ml
$\frac{2}{3}$ oz	firmly packed fresh mint leaves, finely chopped	20 g

In small saucepan, combine sugar, vinegar, water and cornflour; bring to boil over medium heat, stirring constantly. Stir in mint; simmer for 3 minutes.

Transfer to sauce boat and let stand for 30 minutes to develop flavours. Refrigerate any leftovers (up to 2 months). Makes about 4 fl oz (125 ml).

PER 1 tbsp(15 ml) SERVING

calories   21
g fat   0

g protein   0
g carbohydrate   6

Homemade Ketchup

This tastes delicious, is easy to make and is much lower in salt than commercial ketchup.

1	can (5½ oz [156 ml]) tomato purée	
1 oz	packed brown sugar	25
2 fl oz	water	60 m
2 tbsp	cider vinegar	30 m
¼ tsp	dry mustard	1 m
¼ tsp	cinnamon	1 m
Pinch	each cloves and allspice	Pinc

In jar or bowl, combine tomato purée, sugar, water, vinegar, mustard, cinnamon, cloves and allspice; mix well. Cover and store in refrigerator for up to 1 month. Makes about 8 fl oz (250 ml).

PER 1 tbsp (15 ml) SERVING	
calories	22
g fat	0
g protein	0.5
g carbohydrate	5

Sauce recipes, see also

Marinades, see

Compare

per tbsp (15 ml)	mg sodium
This recipe	9
Commercial ketchup	170

Preparing and Sealing Jars for Preserves

Use glass jars with tight-fitting lids. Assemble the number of jars required, plus one extra in case there is a little more preserve than expected.

Wash jars in hot soapy water; rinse and set upright on a metal tray or sturdy baking sheet along with metal tongs, a heatproof measure or ladle and a wide-mouthed metal funnel.

About 20 minutes before the preserve is ready, heat prepared equipment on tray in 225°F (110°C) Gas Mark ½ oven for 15 minutes. Leave all equipment in turned-off oven until needed.

Place lids and screw bands in small saucepan; cover with boiling water and boil for 5 minutes just before sealing jars or follow manufacturer's instructions.

Using ladle or measuring cup pour preserve through funnel into jars, leaving ¼ in (5 mm) headspace. Seal immediately. Wipe cooled, sealed jars and label. Store in a cool dark place for up to one year.

To Seal with Paraffin Wax

Melt paraffin wax in an old double boiler over simmering water or in a microwave-safe container with pouring spout using medium (50%) power. Pour thin layer of paraffin over preserve; tilt and rotate jar to extend seal to rim. Let cool and apply second thin layer in similar manner.

DESSERTS, CAKES AND BREADS

When I take the time to bake or make a dessert I want it to taste really delicious. Homemade biscuits may have to be a little higher in fat than I would like but there is no sense making low-fat biscuits that nobody eats. You can make some adjustments to a recipe to make it more nutritious, such as using wholemeal flour instead of all-purpose and keeping sugar to a minimum. Most homemade biscuits, as long as you use a recommended margarine or oil, are going to be lower in saturated fat than commercial biscuits.

Too many rich desserts can add a huge amount of saturated fat and calories to your diet. There are desserts, however, that taste wonderful and are also low in fat. Instead of trying to make a low-fat chocolate mousse, try a fresh strawberry mousse; instead of an apple pie make an apple crisp. Imitation nondairy creams and toppings could be worse for you, as they often contain saturated fats (palm and coconut oils). Fresh fruits in season are one of the best desserts for any type of meal.

Recipe Modification for Baked Goods
It is critical to understand the purpose of an ingredient before you change it.
- Flour forms the network of a baked product. In most recipes, to increase the fibre, you can substitute one-half the amount of plain flour for a less refined flour, e.g. wholemeal.
- Shortening such as lard and other fats add tenderness, crispness, lightness and volume. All sources of animal fat, plus coconut and palm oil and hydrogenated fats, should be avoided and replaced with unsaturated products.
- Sugar and other sweeteners add flavour, colour, tenderness and crispness and can sometimes be reduced without affecting the quality of a product. Flavours that give the illusion of sweetness (without adding calories) are cinnamon nutmeg and vanilla.
- Liquids act as solvents for other ingredients as well as activating chemical reactions. Low-fat liquids that can be substituted are water, fruit juice, skimmed milk or buttermilk
- Eggs form the network of baked goods, adding flavour, colour and moisture. You can often substitute two egg whites for one whole egg.
- Salt adds flavour and acts as a catalyst that controls chemical reactions. Salt is necessary to the yeast reaction in baking bread but there is no need for salt in baked goods that call for margarine as margarine already contains salt.

Banana and Raisin Muffins

Oat bran is available in the cereal section in most supermarkets. It is an excellent source of the kind of fibre that may help lower blood cholesterol; wheat bran doesn't have the same cholesterol-lowering effect. (Recipe pictured opposite page 152.)

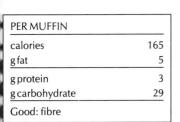

PER MUFFIN	
calories	165
g fat	5
g protein	3
g carbohydrate	29
Good: fibre	

1	egg, lightly beaten	1
4 fl oz	milk	125 ml
2 fl oz	vegetable oil	60 ml
3½ oz	granulated sugar	90 g
7 oz	mashed bananas	180 g
1 tsp	vanilla	5 ml
5 oz	wholemeal flour	125 g
1 tsp	baking soda	5 ml
1 tsp	baking powder	5 ml
2 oz	oat bran	50 g
4 oz	raisins	100 g

In bowl, combine egg, milk, oil, sugar, bananas and vanilla; mix well. In another bowl, mix together flour, baking soda, baking powder, oat bran and raisins; stir into egg mixture, mixing only until combined.

Spoon into 12 nonstick or paper-lined muffin tins, filling each about ⅔ full. Bake in 400°F (200°C) Gas Mark 6 oven for 20 to 25 minutes or until firm to the touch. Makes 12 muffins.

Applesauce and Raisin Squares

Cinnamon and lemon add extra flavour to these moist, cakelike squares. (Recipe pictured opposite page 152.)

PER SQUARE	
calories	88
g fat	3
g protein	2
g carbohydrate	14

1	egg	
2 fl oz	vegetable oil	60 m
5 oz	low-fat natural yogurt	125
3½ oz	brown sugar	90
9 oz	apple, unpeeled and sliced	230
1 tsp	vanilla essence	5 m
1 tsp	grated lemon rind	5 m
3 oz	raisins	75
10 oz	wholemeal flour	250
1 tsp	baking powder	5 m
2 tsp	cinnamon	10 m
1 tsp	ginger	5 m
¼ tsp	ground nutmeg	1 m
2 oz	sliced almonds	50

In a small saucepan, add 1 tbsp (15 ml) of water to the sliced apples and simmer gently until soft.

In large mixing bowl, beat egg; add oil, yogurt, brown sugar, stewed apple, vanilla and lemon rind; mix well.

In another bowl, stir together raisins, flour, baking powder, cinnamon, ginger and nutmeg; add to wet ingredients and mix only until combined.

Turn into lightly greased 8 in (2 lit) square cake tin. Lightly press almonds into top of batter. Bake in 350°F (180°C) Gas Mark 4 oven for 45 minutes or until tester inserted in centre comes out clean. (Squares will be moist.) Let cool, then cut into squares. Makes 25 1½ in (4 cm) squares.

Oatmeal and Apricot Biscuits

I test how good biscuits are by how long they stay around my house. These passed with flying colours because they were all gone in a few hours. They are much lower in fat and higher in fibre than most biscuits.

PER BISCUIT	
calories	52
g fat	2
g protein	1
g carbohydrate	1

3 oz	unsaturated margarine	75 g
7 oz	brown sugar	175 g
1	egg	1
4 fl oz	skimmed milk	125 ml
1 tsp	vanilla essence	5 ml
5 oz	wholemeal flour	125 g
1 tsp	baking powder	5 ml
½ tsp	baking soda	2 ml
½ tsp	cinnamon	2 ml
4 oz	rolled oats	100 g
3 tbsp	wheat germ	45 ml
8 oz	chopped dried apricots (or dates, raisins or a combination)	200 g

In large mixing bowl, combine margarine, sugar and egg; beat well. Beat in milk and vanilla. Add flour, baking powder, baking soda, cinnamon, rolled oats, wheat germ and raisins; mix well.

Drop mixture a small spoonful at a time onto nonstick baking sheet. Bake in 375°F (190°C) Gas Mark 5 oven for 12 to 15 minutes or until golden. Makes about 50 biscuits.

Oat bran, an excellent source of soluble fibre, may help to reduce blood cholesterol.

Easy Oat Bran and Date Biscuits

These easy-to-make, crisp biscuits are a favourite in our house. Oat bran is available in the cereal section of most supermarkets. (Recipe pictured opposite page 152.)

PER BISCUIT (made with coconut)	
calories	97
g fat	4
g protein	1
g carbohydrate	14

6 oz	unsaturated margarine	150 g
7 oz	brown sugar	175 g
1	egg, slightly beaten	1
1 tbsp	water	15 m
5 oz	wholemeal flour	125 g
2 oz	oat bran	50 g
3 tbsp	wheat germ	45 m
1 tsp	baking soda	5 m
1 tsp	baking powder	5 m
8 oz	chopped dates or raisins	225 g
2 oz	chopped nuts, chocolate chips or coconut (optional)	50 g

In large bowl, cream margarine, brown sugar, egg and water together thoroughly. Add flour, oat bran, wheat germ, baking soda and baking powder; mix well. Stir in dates or raisins, and nuts (if using).

Drop mixture by spoonfuls onto lightly greased baking sheets; flatten slightly with floured fork. Bake in 350°F (180°C) Gas Mark 4 oven for 15 minutes or until light golden. Makes about 3 dozen biscuits.

PER SLICE	
calories	128
g fat	3
g protein	4
g carbohydrate	22
Good: fibre	

iouring milk

nstead of buttermilk, you can
substitute soured milk. To sour
milk add 1 tbsp (15 ml) white
vinegar to 8 fl oz (250 ml) milk.

Five-Grain Soda Bread

This is a quick and easy bread to make. It's particularly good
served hot with brunch or with bean dishes, such as Bean
Casserole with Tomatoes and Spinach (page 106). If you don't
have all of these flours, use a combination of what you have.
(Recipe pictured opposite page 152.)

$4\frac{1}{2}$ oz	plain, white flour	120 g
4 oz	each wholemeal flour, rye flour, whole wheat flour and rolled oats	100 g
2 tbsp	granulated sugar	30 ml
1 tbsp	baking powder	15 ml
1 tsp	baking soda	5 ml
$\frac{1}{2}$ tsp	salt	2 ml
3 tbsp	unsaturated margarine or vegetable oil	45 ml
6 oz	raisins (optional)	150 g
14 fl oz	buttermilk	425 ml

In bowl, combine wholemeal, rye and whole wheat flours,
rolled oats, sugar, baking powder, baking soda and salt; cut in
margarine until well mixed. Stir in raisins (if using), add
buttermilk and stir to make soft dough.

Turn out onto lightly floured surface and knead about 10 times
or until smooth. Place on greased baking sheet; flatten into
circle about $2\frac{1}{2}$ in (6 cm) thick. Cut large "X" about $\frac{1}{4}$ in (5 mm)
deep on top.

Bake in 350°F (180°C) Gas Mark 4 oven for 1 hour or until
toothpick inserted in centre comes out clean. Makes 1 loaf
(about 16 slices).

Wholemeal and Oatmeal Bread

Wholemeal bread has three times the fibre of white bread, more protein and much more flavour.

PER SLICE	
calories	83
g fat	1.5
g protein	3
g carbohydrate	15

8 fl oz	skimmed milk	250 m
1½ oz	packed brown sugar	40
2 tbsp	vegetable oil	30 m
½ tsp	salt	2 m
1 tsp	granulated sugar	5 m
8 fl oz	warm water	250 m
1	pkg active dry yeast (or 1 tbsp [15 ml])	
20 oz	(approx.) wholemeal flour	550
4 oz	rolled oats	100
3 tbsp	wheat germ (optional)	45 m

Topping

1	egg white	
1 tbsp	skimmed milk	15 m
1 tsp	dill seeds	5 m
1 tsp	celery seeds	5 m
2 tbsp	rolled oats	30 m

Variation

Food Processor Method: Halve recipe, except use the same amount of yeast (1 pkg or 1 tbsp [15 ml]). Dissolve granulated sugar and yeast as directed.

In food processor fitted with metal or dough blade, combine flour, rolled oats, and wheat germ (if using), brown sugar and salt; process to combine. Stir oil into dissolved yeast mixture; add to flour -mixture and process for 5 seconds.

With machine running, gradually add cold milk; process until dough forms ball, about 45 seconds. If dough is too dry, add more water 1 tbsp (15 ml) at a time. If too sticky, add more flour a little at a time and process with off-on turns. Transfer dough to greased bowl and follow above recipe.

In saucepan (or large bowl and in microwave), heat milk until hot; stir in brown sugar, oil and salt until blended and sugar has dissolved. Let cool to lukewarm.

In small bowl, dissolve granulated sugar in warm water; sprinkle yeast over top and let stand for 10 minutes or until foamy.

In large bowl, combine milk mixture and yeast mixture. Using electric mixer or by hand, gradually beat in 15 fl oz (375 g) of the flour; beat for 2 to 3 minutes or until smooth.

Gradually mix in rolled oats and wheat germ (if using); add enough of the remaining flour to make medium-stiff dough. Turn out onto lightly floured surface and knead until smooth and elastic, about 10 minutes. (If dough is sticky, knead in more flour.)

Place dough in lightly greased bowl, turning to grease all sides. Cover bowl with greased plastic wrap. Let rise in warm place until doubled in bulk, about 1 hour.

Punch down dough and turn out onto lightly floured surface. Divide in half, forming each half into smooth ball. Cover and let rest for 10 minutes.

Shape each half into round or rectangular shape; place rectangular shapes in 2 greased 8 × 4 in (1.5 lit) loaf tins; place round shapes on baking sheet. Cover with plastic bag or greased waxed paper; let rise until doubled in bulk, about 1 hour.

Topping: In small bowl, mix egg white with milk; brush over top of dough. Combine dill seeds, celery seeds and rolled oats; sprinkle over dough.

Bake in 400°F (200°C) Gas Mark 6 oven for 15 minutes; reduce heat to 350°F (180°C) Gas Mark 4 and bake for 20 to 25 minutes longer or until crusts are brown and loaves sound hollow when tapped on bottom. Remove from tins and let cool on racks. Makes 2 loaves, about 16 slices each.

Wholemeal Courgette Bread

This version of courgette bread is lower in fat than most, yet it is moist and full of flavour.

PER SLICE	
calories	152
g fat	4
g protein	3
g carbohydrate	27

7½ oz	plain flour	200
7½ oz	wholemeal flour	200
1 tbsp	cinnamon	15 n
1 tsp	nutmeg	5 n
1 tsp	baking soda	5 n
1 tsp	baking powder	5 n
½ tsp	salt	2 n
5 oz	raisins	125
2	eggs	
5 tbsp	vegetable oil	75 n
5 oz	low-fat natural yogurt	125
2 fl oz	milk	60 n
7 oz	brown sugar	175
2 tsp	vanilla	10 n
10 oz	finely shredded unpeeled courgette	240

In bowl, combine plain and wholemeal flours, cinnamon, nutmeg, baking soda, baking powder, salt and raisins.

In large bowl, beat eggs until foamy; beat in oil, yogurt, milk, sugar and vanilla. Stir in courgettes. Add flour mixture and stir until combined.

Pour batter into 2 well-greased 8×4 in (1.5 lit) loaf tins. Bake in 350°F (180°C) Gas Mark 4 oven for 55 minutes or until toothpick inserted in centre comes out clean. Remove from tin and let cool thoroughly before slicing. Makes 2 loaves (about 1: slices each).

Right:
Easy Oat Bran and Date Biscuits (page 148), Banana and Raisin Muffins (page 145), Apple Cake (page 174), Five-Grain Soda Bread (page 149), Applesauce and Raisin Squares (page 146)

Homemade Crispbread

Arrange this crisp, thin bread, or crackers, in a wicker basket and serve with salads or soups, or break into small pieces and use instead of crisps for dipping.

PER 5 PIECES	
calories	96
g fat	4.5
g protein	3
g carbohydrate	12

2½ oz	sesame seeds	60 g
3 oz	cracked wheat	75 g
4½ oz	plain, white flour	120 g
5 oz	wholemeal flour	135 g
1 tbsp	granulated sugar	15 ml
½ tsp	salt	2 ml
½ tsp	baking soda	2 ml
2½ oz	unsaturated margarine	60 g
7 fl oz	buttermilk	200 ml
Topping		
1	egg white	1
1 tbsp	water	15 ml
2 tbsp	poppyseeds	30 ml

In bowl, combine sesame seeds, cracked wheat, plain and wholemeal flours, sugar, salt, baking soda; cut in margarine. Add buttermilk; mix well.

Shape into 6 balls about the size of a lemon; roll out on lightly floured surface into circles less than ⅛ in (3 mm) thick (as thin as you can). Using spatula, transfer to ungreased baking sheet.

Topping: Combine egg white and water; brush over top of circles. Sprinkle with poppyseeds. Bake in 400°F (200°C) Gas Mark 6 oven for 10 minutes or until golden brown.

Let cool on wire rack until crisp. Break in smaller pieces and store in airtight container. Makes 24 servings (about 5 pieces each).

eft:
wordfish Steaks with Lime
nd Coriander (page 104)

PER PLAIN CRÊPE	
calories	39
g fat	0.5
g protein	2
g carbohydrate	7

Variation

Dessert crêpes: For dessert crêpes, add 2 tsp (10 ml) granulated sugar, $\frac{1}{2}$ tsp (2 ml) each grated orange and lemon rind to batter.

PER DESSERT CRÊPE	
calories	44
g fat	0.5
g protein	2
g carbohydrate	8

Basic Crêpes

This all-purpose crêpe batter is low in fat. Use 2 whites instead of a whole egg. Prepare a batch of crêpes when you have time; freeze them and you'll be able to make a main course such as Curried Chicken Crêpes or a luscious dessert of Peach Crêpes with Grand Marnier Sauce at a moment's notice.

$2\frac{1}{2}$ oz	plain, white flour	60
Pinch	salt	Pinch
2	egg whites, lightly beaten	
$2\frac{1}{2}$ fl oz	skimmed milk	75 m
$2\frac{1}{2}$ fl oz	water	75 m
$\frac{1}{2}$ tsp	unsaturated margarine	2 m

In bowl, combine flour and salt. Make a well in centre and add egg whites. While whisking, gradually add milk and water, whisking until mixture is smooth.

Heat small nonstick pan or crêpe pan (6 to 8 in [15 to 20 cm]) over medium-high heat. Add margarine and brush over bottom of pan. Add 1 to 2 tbsp (15 to 30 ml) of batter and swirl to cover bottom of pan. You should have just enough batter to lightly coat bottom of pan; pour off any excess. Shake pan and cook until edges begin to curl and crêpe no longer sticks to pan. Turn crêpe and cook for a few seconds or until golden. Remove from pan and set aside. Repeat with remaining batter. You shouldn't need to add any more margarine.

Crêpes can be made in advance; stack between waxed paper and refrigerate for 1 day or freeze up to 1 month. Makes 8 (8 in [20 cm]) crêpes.

Blackcurrant Cream Flan

No one will ever guess that this cheesecake-type dessert is made with yogurt or low-fat fromage frais.

7 oz	plain, white flour	180 g
3½ oz	granulated sugar	90 g
1½ tsp	baking powder	7 ml
2½ oz	unsaturated margarine	60 g
2	egg whites	2
1 tsp	vanilla	5 ml
1½ lb	blackcurrants, fresh or frozen (not thawed)	675 g

Topping

2 tbsp	plain, white flour	30 ml
18 oz	low-fat natural yogurt or fromage frais	500 g
1	egg, lightly beaten	1
5 oz	granulated sugar	125 g
2 tsp	grated lemon or orange rind	10 ml
1 tsp	vanilla	5 ml

PER PIECE	
calories	232
g fat	6
g protein	5
g carbohydrate	40

   In food processor or mixing bowl, combine flour, sugar, baking powder, margarine, egg whites and vanilla; mix well. Press into bottom of 10 in (3 lit) square cake tin, or flan dish; sprinkle with blackcurrants.
   Topping: In bowl, sprinkle flour over yogurt or fromage frais. Add egg, sugar, rind and vanilla; mix until smooth. Pour over blackcurrants.
   Bake in 350°F (180°C) Gas Mark 4 oven for 60 to 70 minutes or until golden. Serve warm or cold. Makes 12 servings.

Lemon Roll with Fresh Fruit

Serve this light lemon-filled cake roll with whatever fruit is in season — orange and kiwi slices are nice in winter, strawberries in spring, blackberries in summer, peaches or grapes in the autumn.

Lemon Filling

3 tbsp	cornflour	45 m
2½ oz	granulated sugar	60
1 tsp	grated lemon rind	5 m
2½ fl oz	lemon juice	75 m
6 fl oz	water	180 m
1	egg yolk	
1 tbsp	unsaturated margarine	15 m

Cake

5	egg whites	
⅛ tsp	salt	0.5 m
⅛ tsp	cream of tartar	0.5 m
3½ oz	granulated sugar	90
2 oz	sifted self-raising flour	50
2 tsp	lemon juice	10 m
½ tsp	vanilla essence	2 m
¼ tsp	almond essence	1 m
3 tbsp	icing sugar	45 m

Garnish

2	oranges, peeled and sliced	
2	kiwi, peeled and sliced	
	OR	
2 lb	strawberries or blackberries	900

Lemon Filling: In small saucepan, combine cornflour with sugar: whisk in lemon rind, juice and water. Bring to boil over medium heat, stirring constantly, and cook for 2 minutes or until thickened and smooth. Blend a little of the hot mixture into egg yolk; stir yolk mixture into saucepan. Cook over low heat, stirring constantly, for 2 minutes. Remove from heat and stir in margarine. Let cool, stirring frequently to prevent skin from forming on top.

Portable Picnic Dessert

Take to picnic a container of sliced strawberries sprinkled with a small amount of sugar, a container of natural yogurt and a small jar of brown sugar. Also pack some clear plastic glasses and spoons. Spoon strawberries into glasses, top with yogurt and sprinkle with brown sugar.

For maximum flavour be sure to serve fruit, including berries, at room temperature, not straight from the refrigerator.

Cake: Line 15 × 10 in (2 lit) Swiss roll tin or baking sheet with foil; thoroughly grease and flour.

In large bowl, beat egg whites, salt and cream of tartar just until mixture mounds on spoon (not quite to soft peak stage). Using spatula, fold in granulated sugar, a large spoonful at a time. Sift half of the flour over egg-white mixture and fold in gently; repeat with remaining flour. Fold in lemon juice, vanilla and almond essence.

Spread in prepared tin; bake in 300°F (150°C) Gas Mark 2 oven for 25 minutes or until firm to the touch. (Cake will be light in colour.)

Sift half of icing sugar over cake; cover with tea towel then inverted baking sheet. Turn cake over and carefully remove Swiss roll tin. Trim any crusty edges. While cake is hot, roll up in towel, starting at long side, Swiss roll fashion; let cool. (Cake and filling can be prepared to this point, covered and refrigerated for up to 1 day.)

Unroll cake and spread evenly with lemon filling. Roll up cake using towel to help roll. Sift remaining icing sugar over top. Place seam-side-down on serving platter. Just before serving arrange slices of fresh orange and kiwi around lemon roll. Makes 8 servings.

What to Pour over Dessert

	fat (g)	kCals	energy kJ
Cream	per 4 oz (100 g)		
Half cream	12	140	588
Single cream	18	200	840
Soured cream	18	285	1197
Whipping cream	35	360	1512
Double cream	48	444	1865
Clotted cream	55	592	2486
Sterilized, canned			
Full fat	23	295	1239
Half fat	12	140	588
Half fat cream			
eg Shape Single	9	115	483
Shape Double	16	260	1092
Vegetable fat creams			
eg Elmlea Single	17	197	828
Elmlea Whipping	34	331	1390
Yogurt	per 6 oz (150 g) pot		
Whole milk, fruit	4.5	180	756
Low fat, fruit	1.5	140	588
Low fat, natural	1.5	90	378
Diet, fruit	neg	130	546
Greek Yogurt	10	130	546
Goat's natural	4	85	357
Other similar products:			
Fromage Frais, plain	7.1	113	469
Fromage Frais, fruit	5.8	131	551
Fromage Frais, very low fat	0.2	58	247
Quark	neg	74	313
Buttermilk	1.0	41	173
Custard	per 4 oz (100 g) serving		
Made with whole milk and egg	6.0	118	496
Made with whole milk	4.5	117	495
Made with semi-skimmed milk	1.9	94	403
Made with skimmed milk	0.1	79	339
Tinned pre-prepared	3.0	95	401

Strawberry Mousse

This is a wonderful dinner-party dessert. It's light yet full of flavour, can be prepared in advance and is easy to make.

1	sachet gelatine	
2 fl oz	orange juice	60 m
1½ lb	fresh strawberries	675
1½ oz	icing sugar	40
4 fl oz	whipping cream (optional)	125 m
4	egg whites	
1 oz	granulated sugar	25

Garnish

Fresh strawberries, hulled

Strawberry Mousse Cake

Prepare Strawberry Mousse, as opposite. Cut a sponge cake or a small angel food cake into 2 layers.

Place one layer on serving platter. Spread one-third of strawberry mousse over cake. (If mousse is too firm to spread, let stand at room temperature to soften slightly.) Cover with second cake layer. Spread remaining mousse over top and sides of cake. Refrigerate for up to 8 hours.

Just before serving, arrange fresh strawberries around or over top of cake. Makes 8 servings.

In small microwave-safe dish or saucepan, sprinkle gelatine over orange juice; let stand for 5 minutes to soften. Microwave at medium (50%) power for 30 seconds, or warm over low heat until gelatine has dissolved.

Meanwhile, hull strawberries and place in food processor or blender; add icing sugar and process just until puréed (you should have about 12 fl oz [375 ml]). Transfer to mixing bowl an stir in gelatine mixture. Refrigerate until mixture is consistency of raw egg whites.

Whip cream (if using) and set aside. In large bowl, beat egg whites until soft peaks form; gradually add granulated sugar, beating until stiff peaks form. Whisk about ¼ of the beaten egg whites into strawberry mixture.

Fold strawberry mixture along with whipped cream into remaining beaten egg whites. Pour into 2½ pt (1.5 lit) glass serving bowl or individual stemmed glasses; refrigerate for at least 4 hours or up to 2 days. Garnish with fresh strawberries. Makes 6 servings.

Compare		per serving
Dessert made with:	g fat	calorie
No whipping cream	0	90
4 fl oz (120 ml) whipping cream	4	128
12 fl oz (375 ml) whipping cream	13	206

Hot Apricot Soufflé

This light dessert is surprisingly easy to make — and no one will guess that it's low in calories and fat. Try to buy the apricots that are canned in natural juice.

PER SERVING	
calories	91
g fat	0
g protein	4
g carbohydrate	20
Good: vitamin A	

1	can (14 oz [398 g]) apricot halves in natural juice	1
$\frac{1}{2}$ tsp	grated lemon rind	2 ml
1 tsp	lemon juice	5 ml
2 tbsp	granulated sugar	30 ml
4	egg whites	4
$\frac{1}{4}$ tsp	cream of tartar	1 ml
1 tsp	cornflour	5 ml

Drain apricots; place between paper towels and pat dry. In food processor or blender, purée apricots, lemon rind, lemon juice and sugar.

In large bowl, beat egg whites and cream of tartar until stiff peaks form; sift cornflour over whites and fold in. Add about $\frac{1}{4}$ of the beaten whites to apricot mixture and pulse 4 times or mix just until combined. Add apricot mixture to remaining beaten whites and fold together.

Pour into ungreased 3 pt (2 lit) soufflé dish. Bake in 350°F (180°C) Gas Mark 4 oven for 30 to 35 minutes or until puffed and golden brown. Serve immediately. Makes 4 servings.

Streusel Cake

This is a lovely cake to serve for a special Sunday-night dinner or for dessert when you have guests. I like it because it isn't too sweet, yet it's moist and full of flavour. The glaze is optional — it only takes a minute to prepare, makes the cake look fancy yet adds only a few more calories. (Recipe pictured opposite page 184.)

	PER PIECE	
	calories	288
	g fat	8
	g protein	4
	g carbohydrate	50

2 oz	unsaturated margarine	50 g
5½ oz	granulated sugar	135 g
2	eggs, separated	2
7 oz	plain, white flour	180 g
1 tsp	baking powder	5 ml
4 fl oz	skimmed milk	125 ml
2	cans (each 14 oz [398 g]) plums, drained	2

Streusel Topping

3½ oz	brown sugar	90 g
1 tbsp	unsaturated margarine	15 ml
1 tsp	cinnamon	5 ml

Glaze (optional)

1½ oz	icing sugar	40 g
1 tsp	skimmed milk	5 ml
¼ tsp	vanilla essence	1 ml

Grease 9 in (2.5 lit) square cake tin.*

In large bowl, cream together margarine, sugar and egg yolks until fluffy. Combine flour and baking powder; beat into egg mixture alternately with milk. Beat egg whites until stiff but not dry: fold into mixture. Turn into prepared tin. Halve and pit plums and arrange over top.

Streusel topping: In small bowl, combine brown sugar, margarine and cinnamon; mix well and sprinkle over fruit.

Bake in 350°F (180°C) Gas Mark 4 oven for 35 to 45 minutes or until top is golden and toothpick inserted into cake comes out clean.

Variations

Peach Streusel Cake: Instead of plums use 2 fresh peaches, sliced into wedges or 1 can (14 oz [398 ml]) sliced peaches, thoroughly drained.

Apple Streusel Cake: Instead of plums use 2 apples, sliced into thin wedges. (If apples are unpeeled the fibre content is higher.)

Pear Streusel Cake: Instead of plums use 2 pears, sliced into wedges or 1 can (14 oz [398 ml]) sliced pears, thoroughly drained.

Glaze: Combine icing sugar, milk and vanilla essence; mix well. Drizzle over cool cake. Makes 10 servings.

*Cake Tin Size:
I sometimes use a 10 in (25 cm) cake tin because I like a thinner cake. However, a 9 or 8 in (22 or 20 cm) tin also works well but will take a longer cooking time. If you are using a 10 in (25 cm) tin and canned fruit you can use a 19 oz (540 ml) can.

Peach Crêpes with Grand Marnier Sauce

This dessert is a favourite any time of year but is particularly good in peach season. For a fancy dessert, it is surprisingly low in calories.

5 oz	low-fat natural yogurt	125 g
1 tbsp	honey	15 ml
3	fresh peaches, peeled and sliced	3
8	Dessert Crêpes (page 154)	8

Grand Marnier Sauce

6 fl oz	orange juice	180 ml
1 tbsp	cornflour	15 ml
3 tbsp	Grand Marnier, Drambuie or other orange liqueur	45 ml

Garnish

	Sliced peaches, or other juicy fresh fruit	

PER CRÊPE	
calories	97
g fat	1
g protein	3
g carbohydrate	20
Good: vitamin C	

Grand Marnier Sauce: In saucepan, combine orange juice with cornflour; whisk until smooth. Cook over medium heat, stirring constantly, until mixture thickens and comes to boil; simmer for 2 minutes. Remove from heat and stir in liqueur.

In bowl, combine yogurt with syrup or honey; stir until smooth. Add peaches and mix lightly.

Wrap crêpes in paper towels and heat in microwave at high (100%) power for 30 seconds. Or heat in 350°F (180°C) Gas Mark 4 oven for 5 to 10 minutes or until warm.

Spoon some peach mixture onto each crêpe; roll up and place on individual plates. Drizzle with warm sauce and garnish with fresh fruit. Makes 8 crêpes (4 large or 8 small servings).

Variations
Jiffy Peach Dessert: Sweeten yogurt with honey and spoon over sliced peaches.

Peaches and Blackberries with Grand Marnier Sauce: Spoon Grand Marnier Sauce (see this page) over sliced peaches and blackberries.

Bananas and Kiwi with Grand Marnier Sauce: Spoon sauce over sliced bananas and kiwi.

Apricot Yogurt Parfaits

Enjoy this rich-tasting, easy-to-make dessert without any pangs
of guilt — it's healthy and low-calorie.

1	can (14 oz [398 g]) apricots in natural juice	1
1	sachet gelatine	1
2 tbsp	lemon juice	30 ml
2 tbsp	apricot brandy	30 ml
9 oz	low-fat natural yogurt	230 g
8 oz	fresh apricot slices, kiwi or berries	200 g
Garnish		
	Yogurt, brown sugar or mint leaves	

PER SERVING	
calories	140
g fat	1
g protein	5
g carbohydrate	25
Good: vitamin A, vitamin C, fibre	

Drain apricots, pouring 2 fl oz (60 ml) of the juice into
saucepan or microwave-safe dish. Sprinkle gelatine over juice
and let stand for 5 minutes to soften. Warm over low heat or
microwave at medium (50%) power for 30 seconds or until
gelatine has dissolved.

In food processor or blender, purée apricots; add lemon juice,
brandy, yogurt and gelatine mixture and process for 30 seconds
or until combined.

Pour into stemmed glasses or champagne flutes. Cover and
refrigerate until set, at least 1 hour or overnight.

Just before serving, arrange fruit on top. Garnish each with
small spoonful of yogurt and sprinkling of brown sugar or mint
leaf. Makes 4 servings.

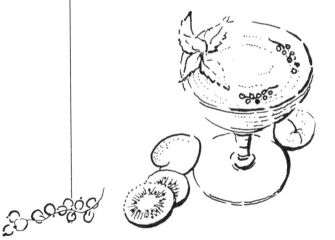

Iced Raspberry Mousse

This make-ahead dessert looks very pretty served in small ramekins or a soufflé dish. You can also chill it in a mould, unmould and surround with fresh fruit then garnish with mint leaves and flowers.

2	sachets gelatine	2
4 fl oz	water	125 ml
1	pkg (425 g) frozen raspberries in natural juice	1
7 oz	low-fat natural yogurt	175 g
$\frac{1}{2}$ tsp	grated orange rind	2 ml
3	egg whites	3
3 oz	granulated sugar	75 g

Garnish

	Fresh raspberries, mint leaves, flowers

In saucepan or microwave-safe dish, sprinkle gelatine over water; let stand for 5 minutes to soften. Heat over low heat or microwave at medium (50%) power for 50 seconds or until gelatine has dissolved.

In food processor or blender, purée raspberries (if using unsweetened, add about 1 oz [25 g] sugar). Transfer to bowl and stir in gelatine mixture, yogurt and orange rind. Refrigerate until mixture begins to set or is consistency of raw egg whites.

In large bowl, beat egg whites until soft peaks form. Gradually add sugar, beating until stiff peaks form. Whisk about $\frac{1}{4}$ of beaten whites into raspberry mixture; fold in remaining whites.

Divide among prepared dishes. Cover and refrigerate for at least 1 hour before serving. Garnish with raspberries, fresh mint and flowers. Makes 6 servings.

PER SERVING	
calories	169
g fat	1
g protein	6
g carbohydrate	37
Good: vitamin C	
Excellent: fibre	

To serve as a soufflé

Cut 8 pieces of waxed paper in (10 cm) wide and slightly longer than circumference of oz (175 g) ramekins or soufflé dishes, demitasse or espresso coffee cups. (Or cut 1 strip for $\frac{1}{2}$ pt [1 lit] soufflé dish.) Fold in half lengthwise. Using tring, tie each strip around outside of dish so 1 in (2.5 cm) extends above rim. Divide raspberry mousse mixture among prepared dishes and refrigerate for at least 1 hour before serving.

Note

Don't strain raspberry purée mixtures. Raspberries, including the seeds, are an excellent source of fibre.

PER SERVING	
calories	109
g fat	0
g protein	0.5
g carbohydrate	28
Excellent: vitamin C	

Raspberry Sorbet
In food processor purée 1 package (9 oz [250 g]) frozen sweetened raspberries, thawed. Add 4 fl oz (125 ml) water and 1½ tsp (7 ml) lemon juice. Freeze according to instructions on page 165. Makes 4 servings.

Variation
Frozen Blackcurrant Snow
Prepare Blackcurrant Sorbet. When mixture is cold, process in food processor with 1 egg white until frothy and light in colour.

PER SERVING	
calories	106
g fat	0
g protein	0.5
g carbohydrate	27
Excellent: vitamin C	

Sherbets, Sorbets, Ices

Whether you can call them sherbets, sorbets or ices, a light refreshing frozen mixture of fresh fruit is the dessert I order most often in restaurants. The desserts are extremely easy to make, especially if you have an ice-cream maker. For a special dinner, serve a combination of sherbets plus fresh berries. Here is a selection to make year-round.

Rhubarb and Strawberry Sorbet

(Recipe pictured opposite page 200)

1 lb	sliced fresh rhubarb	450 g
7 oz	granulated sugar	200 g
12 fl oz	water	375 ml
1 lb	strawberries	450 g
1 tbsp	lemon juice	15 ml
1 tsp	grated orange rind or 2 tbsp (30 ml) orange liqueur	5 ml

In saucepan, combine rhubarb, sugar and half of the water; simmer, covered, until rhubarb is very tender. Purée in food processor; transfer to bowl.

In food processor, purée strawberries; stir into rhubarb mixture. Add lemon juice, orange rind and remaining water.

Freeze according to instructions on page 165. Makes 8 servings.

Blackcurrant Sorbet

(Recipe pictured opposite page 200)

12 oz	blackcurrants (fresh or frozen)	300 g
3½ oz	granulated sugar	90 g
4 fl oz	water	125 ml
8 fl oz	orange juice	250 ml
1 tbsp	lemon juice	15 ml

In saucepan, combine blackcurrants, sugar, water, orange and lemon juices; simmer for 10 minutes. Chill, then freeze according to instructions on page 165. Makes 6 servings.

Freezing and Serving Instructions for Sorbets

Freeze in ice-cream maker following manufacturer's instructions. Alternatively, transfer to metal pan or bowl and freeze until barely firm. Then either process in food processor or beat with electric mixer until smooth. Transfer to freezer container and freeze until firm.

To Serve

Remove from freezer 15 to 30 minutes before serving or until mixture is soft enough to scoop. Serve on dessert plates surrounded with fresh berries or in sherbet glasses, each garnished with its own fruit or fresh mint leaf.

Kiwi Sorbet

12	kiwifruit	12
7 oz	granulated sugar	200 g
8 fl oz	water	250 ml
1 tbsp	lemon juice	15 ml

Using sharp knife, peel kiwi; purée in food processor or pass through fine sieve and place in bowl.

In saucepan, bring sugar, water and lemon juice to boil, stirring occasionally until sugar has dissolved. Add to kiwi and mix well.

Freeze according to instructions on this page. Makes 10 servings.

Pineapple and Orange Sorbet

(Recipe pictured opposite page 200)

4 fl oz	water	125 ml
3½ oz	granulated sugar	100 g
1	pineapple or 1 can (19 oz [540 g]) crushed pineapple in natural juice	1
16 fl oz	orange juice	500 ml
2 tsp	grated orange rind	10 ml
1 tbsp	lemon or lime juice	15 ml

In saucepan, combine water and sugar; simmer until sugar dissolves. Peel pineapple and cut into quarters; purée quarters or undrained pineapple in food processor.

In bowl, combine sugar syrup, orange juice, pineapple, orange rind and lemon juice. Freeze according to instructions on this page. Makes 10 servings.

PER SERVING	
calories	213
g fat	1
g protein	3
g carbohydrate	52
Excellent: fibre, vitamin C	

Sorbet, Fresh Fruit and Fruit Sauce Combinations
There are countless variations of sorbet (sherbets), fresh fruit and sauces you can use.
Consider
Kiwi Sorbet (page 165); fresh sliced kiwi and peaches, Raspberry Sauce
Blackcurrant Sorbet (page 164); fresh raspberries and Raspberry Wine Sauce (page 172)
Pineapple and Orange Sorbet (page 165); sliced oranges, Raspberry Wine Sauce (page 172) or Raspberry Sauce
Rhubarb and Strawberry Sorbet (page 164); blackberries, Raspberry Sauce

Strawberry Sauce
Make Raspberry Sauce but substitute strawberries for raspberries. If sweetened, omit honey or sugar. Use fresh or frozen strawberries.

Strawberry Meringue Parfait
If you have extra meringue, make this wonderful, easy dessert. Break meringue into pieces and mix with Frozen Strawberry Yogurt (page 187). Spoon into parfait glasses and drizzle with Strawberry Sauce recipe (see above). Garnish with fresh berries if in season — either strawberry, raspberry, or blackberry.

Strawberry Meringue Tarts with Raspberry Sauce

Individual meringue nests filled with fresh fruit sherbet, covered with juicy berries or sliced fruit and a drizzling of fruit sauce make a delicious and glamorous dessert that is also light and refreshing.

Meringue Nests

3	egg whites, at room temperature	
Pinch	cream of tartar	Pinch
5 oz	granulated sugar	125
½ tsp	vanilla essence	2 m

Filling

1 lb	Rhubarb and Strawberry Sorbet (page 164) or Frozen Strawberry Yogurt (page 187)	450
1 lb	sliced fresh strawberries or other fruit	450

Raspberry Sauce

1	pkg (300 g) frozen unsweetened raspberries	
1 tbsp	(approx) honey or icing sugar	15 m

Meringue nests: In bowl, beat egg whites with cream of tartar until soft peaks form. Gradually add sugar a tbsp at a time, beating until stiff peaks form. Beat in vanilla.

Spoon meringue onto foil-lined baking sheet in six 4 to 5 in (1 to 12 cm) rounds. Using spoon, shape into nests. Bake in 250°F (120°C) Gas Mark ½ oven for 2 hours or until meringues are crisp but not browned and can be removed from foil. If foil sticks, continue baking. Cool, then store in airtight container up to 2 days; freeze for longer storage.

Raspberry Sauce: In food processor, blender or fine sieve, purée raspberries. Stir in honey or sugar, adding more to taste. Cover and refrigerate for up to 2 days.

To serve: Spoon sherbet into meringue nests; spoon fresh fruit over. Pass sauce separately. Makes 6 servings.

This recipe uses the minimum amount of fat — less than half of a standard crisp recipe — while extra flavour is gained through fruits and cinnamon. Oatmeal adds fibre and flavour. Fruit crisps have less fat than fruit pies. For example, see Sunday Chicken Dinner menu (page 169).

Variation

Apple, Pear and Apricot Crisp: Prepare Apple and Raspberry Crisp using 1 lb (450 g) sliced peeled apples, ½ lb (225 g) sliced peeled pears and 2 oz (50 g) coarsely chopped dried apricots.

Apple and Raspberry Crisp

Combining two fruits, such as apple and raspberry, in a crisp adds more flavour and colour to the crisp than if you use one fruit. Depending on the sweetness of the apples you might want to add more sugar.

1½ lb	sliced peeled apples	675 g
1	pkg (300 g) unsweetened frozen raspberries	1
2½ oz	granulated sugar	60 g
2 tbsp	plain, white flour	30 ml
2 tsp	cinnamon	10 ml
Topping		
3 oz	quick-cooking rolled oats	75 g
1½ oz	brown sugar	40 g
1 tsp	cinnamon	5 ml
2 oz	unsaturated margarine	50 g

In 3 pt (2 lit) baking dish, combine apples and raspberries (thawed or frozen). In small bowl, combine sugar, flour and cinnamon; add to fruit and toss to mix.

Topping: Combine rolled oats, sugar and cinnamon. With pastry blender or 2 knives, cut in margarine until crumbly. Sprinkle over top of fruit mixture.

Bake in 350°F (180°C) Gas Mark 4 oven for 55 minutes or microwave at high (100%) power for 15 minutes or until mixture is bubbling and fruit is barely tender. Serve warm or cold. Makes 8 servings.

Rhubarb Stewed with Apple and Strawberries

Combine rhubarb with apple and orange, then add some dried fruit such as raisins or apricots during cooking. Or after cooking, add any other fresh fruit such as kiwi, grapes, banana or strawberries.

PER SERVING	
calories	85
g fat	0.5
g protein	2
g carbohydrate	20
Good: fibre	
Excellent: vitamin C	

1	orange	1
1 lb	fresh or frozen rhubarb	450 g
1	large apple	1
8 fl oz	water	250 m
1 oz	(approx.) granulated sugar	25 g
1 lb	fresh strawberries (optional)	450 g
5 oz	low-fat natural yogurt	125 g
2 tbsp	brown sugar	30 m

Grate rind and squeeze juice from orange. Cut rhubarb into 1 in (2.5 cm) lengths. Peel, core and thinly slice apple.

In saucepan, combine orange rind and juice, rhubarb, apple, water and sugar; cover and bring to boil. Reduce heat and simmer for 10 minutes or until fruit is tender, stirring occasionally. Remove from heat and stir in strawberries. Add more sugar to taste. Serve warm or at room temperature. Top each serving with a spoonful of yogurt and sprinkle with brown sugar. Makes 8 servings.

Compare Dinner 1 and Dinner 2:
A few easy choices in everyday foods can make a big difference in the amount of fat in our diet.

Sunday Chicken Dinner 1	g fat	calories
Roast Chicken (no skin)	8	215
Cranberry sauce	0	38
Baked potato	0	220
with sour cream and yogurt	1	16
Steamed broccoli	0	26
Apple and Raspberry Crisp (page 167)	7	219
Totals	16	734
Calories from fat = 20%		

Fruits to Combine with or Substitute for Berries

Winter: sliced oranges, bananas, kiwi, pineapple, cantaloupe or honeydew melon

Spring: strawberries, stewed rhubarb

Summer: raspberries, blackberries, blackcurrants

Autumn: peaches, plums, grapes

Suggested berry or fruit combinations

grapes and melon; melon and raspberries; blackberries and sliced peaches; raspberries and blackcurrants, strawberries and kiwi; bananas and kiwi or sliced oranges.

PER SERVING	
calories	126
g fat	3
g protein	5
g carbohydrate	24
Good: fibre	
Excellent: vitamin C	

Blackberries with Orange and Honey Yogurt

Any kind of fresh fruit is wonderful with this tasty, easy-to-make sauce. Choose the fruits depending on the season. This looks nice served in stemmed glasses.

2 lb	blackberries or combination of berries	900 g

Garnish

	Fresh mint leaves, thin strips of orange rind or 1 tbsp (15 ml) toasted sliced or slivered almonds	

Orange and Honey Yogurt

9 oz	low-fat natural yogurt	230 g
1 tsp	grated orange rind	5 ml
1 tbsp	orange juice	15 ml
2 tbsp	honey	30 ml
½ tsp	vanilla or almond essence	2 ml

Orange and Honey Yogurt: In bowl, combine yogurt, orange rind, orange juice, honey and vanilla essence; mix well.

Wash berries and hull; slice if large.

Either mix fruit with sauce, cover and refrigerate for 1 hour or, alternatively, at serving time spoon fruit into individual bowls or stemmed glasses and pour sauce over. Garnish each serving with fresh mint leaves, orange rind or almonds. Makes 4 servings.

Sunday Chicken Dinner 2	g fat	calories
Roast Chicken (with skin)	15	271
Gravy	3	34
Mashed potatoes	0	182
with butter and milk	8	70
Steamed broccoli	0	26
Apple pie	18	406
Totals	44	989
Calories from fat = 44%		

Winter Fruit Compôte with Figs and Apricots

Figs, apricots and prunes spiked with rum are a delicious base for an easy compôte. Add the fresh fruits suggested here or any you have on hand such as pineapple or kiwi. You can substitute orange juice for the rum, if desired. For a stronger rum flavour add it to the cooled mixture. (Recipe pictured opposite page 201.)

PER SERVING	
calories	148
g fat	1
g protein	2
g carbohydrate	38
Excellent: fibre, vitamin C	

3 oz	each dried figs, apricots and prunes	75 g
4 fl oz	rum	125 ml
12 fl oz	orange juice	375 ml
12 oz	seedless green grapes	350 g
6 oz	purple or red grapes, halved and seeded	175 g
1	can (10 oz [284 g]) mandarin oranges, undrained	1
1	grapefruit, peeled and sectioned	1

In saucepan, combine dried figs, apricots, prunes, rum and orange juice; cover and bring to boil. Simmer for 10 minutes; remove from heat and let stand for 20 minutes or until fruit is plump and tender. Let cool.

In serving dish, combine fig mixture, green and red grapes, mandarin oranges and grapefruit. Serve immediately or cover and refrigerate up to 3 days. Makes 8 servings.

Oranges in Grand Marnier

This very elegant dessert is one of my favourites. It's a good choice in February and March when navel oranges are so sweet and juicy. Serve with cake or wafer-thin biscuits.

6	oranges	6
2 oz	granulated sugar	50 g
8 fl oz	water	250 ml
3 oz	honey	75 g
2 tbsp	lemon juice	30 ml
2½ fl oz	(approx.) Grand Marnier or Triple Sec liqueur	75 ml

Using very fine grater or vegetable peeler, peel thin strips of orange rind from 2 of the oranges, being careful not to include any white part. Cut into wispy thin strips and place in saucepan. Pour in enough cold water to cover and bring to boil (this removes bitter flavour); drain and set aside.

Using sharp knife, cut peel, including any white pith and membrane, from oranges. Cut oranges into round slices and place in glass bowl or in overlapping slices on serving dish.

In saucepan, combine sugar, water and honey; bring to boil, stirring only until sugar has dissolved. Add strips of orange rind; simmer, uncovered, for 25 minutes or until syrup is slightly thickened. Remove from heat; stir in lemon juice and liqueur. Let cool, then pour over oranges.

Refrigerate for 2 to 8 hours, turning oranges once or twice. Taste and add more liqueur if desired. Makes 6 servings.

Fresh Pineapple Slices with Rum

Juicy, sweet, fresh pineapple spiked with a touch of rum is a quick and easy dessert. For a special occasion, cut pineapple carefully so you can present it in pineapple quarters garnished with strawberries, red grapes, kiwi or other fresh fruits. Serve with a crisp wafer biscuit.

1	pineapple	
3 tbsp	brown sugar	45 m
3 tbsp	rum, preferably dark	45 m

Garnish

	Sliced kiwi fruit, orange segments, grapes or strawberries	

PER SERVING	
calories	87
g fat	0
g protein	0
g carbohydrate	18
Excellent: vitamin C	

Cut top and bottom from pineapple. Cut down sides to remove peel and eyes. Cut pineapple into quarters. If core is tough or pithy, remove. Slice quarters into cubes.

In bowl, toss pineapple with brown sugar and rum; cover and let stand for 30 minutes or refrigerate up to 3 hours.

Serve in frosted sherbet or wine glasses and garnish with fresh fruit. Makes 6 servings.

Raspberry Wine Sauce

Rich with raspberries, this easy-to-make sauce is delicious over ice cream, sherbets or angel cake.

3½ oz	granulated sugar	90 g
1 tbsp	cornflour	15 m
8 fl oz	dry white wine	250 m
1 tbsp	lemon juice	15 m
12 oz	raspberries (fresh or frozen)	350 g

In small saucepan, stir together sugar and cornflour; stir in wine and lemon juice. Cook, stirring constantly, over medium heat until mixture thickens, clears and comes to boil.

Stir in raspberries and simmer, stirring, for 1 minute or until at least half of the berries burst. Let cool and refrigerate. Makes approximately 6 servings.

PER 3 fl oz (90 ml) SERVING	
calories	69
g fat	0
g protein	0
g carbohydrate	18

Fresh Peaches with Banana Cream Whip

For a quick, low-calorie family dessert, serve this on sliced peaches, berries or other fruits or instead of whipped cream. It's best to make it about an hour or less before serving because it will darken upon standing.

1	egg white	1
1	large banana, mashed	1
1 tbsp	icing sugar	15 ml
1 tsp	lemon juice	5 ml
12 oz	sliced fresh peaches or tinned peaches in natural juice	350 g

In small bowl, beat egg white until foamy. Add banana, icing sugar and lemon juice; beat until mixture forms stiff peaks. Spoon peaches into individual dishes; top with Banana Cream. Makes 4 servings.

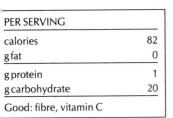

PER SERVING	
calories	82
g fat	0
g protein	1
g carbohydrate	20
Good: fibre, vitamin C	

Apple Cake

This coffeecake-type cake stays moist and is great for brunch, with fruit desserts or packed lunches. I don't peel the apples because the skin adds fibre. (Recipe pictured opposite page 152.)

PER PIECE	
(including coconut)	
calories	192
g fat	5
g protein	4
g carbohydrate	35
Good: fibre	

1½ oz	unsaturated margarine	40 g
4½ oz	brown sugar	130 g
12 fl oz	buttermilk	375 m
4½ oz	plain, white flour	120 g
5 oz	wholemeal flour	135 g
1 tsp	baking powder	5 m
1 tsp	baking soda	5 m
1 tbsp	cinnamon	15 m
½ tsp	salt	2 m
2	medium apples, cored and finely chopped	2

Topping

1 oz	brown sugar	25 g
2 tsp	cinnamon	10 m
2 tbsp	chopped nuts or coconut (optional)	30 m

Lightly grease and flour 8 or 9 in (2 or 2.5 lit) square cake tin.

In large bowl, beat together margarine and sugar until combined; beat in buttermilk. Add flours, baking powder, baking soda, cinnamon, salt and apples; mix until combined. Spread batter evenly in pan.

Topping: Combine sugar, cinnamon and nuts or coconut; sprinkle over batter. Bake in 350°F (180°C) Gas Mark 4 oven for 40 to 45 minutes or until toothpick inserted in centre comes out clean. Let cool in tin. Makes 12 servings.

LIFESTYLE

British Heart Foundation's Dietary Recommendations for the Family

These dietary recommendations are designed for healthy adults. Most school-age children can also follow the recommendations, keeping in mind that it's most important to eat a balanced diet, choosing foods from the four food groups; milk and milk products; breads and cereals; fruits and vegetables; meats and alternates. After the age of five years children can eat a low-fat diet and for those who have a large appetite and are not overweight, healthy snacks between meals may be necessary for them to eat enough energy for growth. Families with a history of heart disease may want to consult their doctor to see if a more restrictive diet is necessary for their children.

Young babies and children to the age of two years should be on full-fat milk if not on breast milk or formula. Consult your doctor, nurse or dietitian for further dietary advice, if needed.

After the age of two, providing they are thriving well, they can be fed on semi-skimmed milk and lower-fat foods can be introduced as part of a mixed family diet.

Feeding Your Family

One of the primary responsibilities of parents is to see that their children are well fed and develop good eating habits. Sometimes this can take all your wits and patience, but it is worth every bit of thought and effort. The sooner children develop good eating habits the healthier they'll be, and the more likely it will be that they'll continue eating well throughout life.

Now that our three children are teenagers, we get a great deal of pleasure from trying new foods together, eating out at ethnic restaurants, and having a nice dinner in the dining room as often as everyone can be home. But this wasn't always the case: I can remember the children screaming with 2-year-old rage because I wouldn't give them a biscuit 20 minutes before dinner; or as 5-year-olds refusing homemade soup but loving it out of a can; or saying "Yuck" to what I thought was delicious homemade stew.

Unhealthy eating may cause behaviour problems, lack of concentration and drowsiness in children. Poor nutrition can be the result of missing breakfast and eating too many fast foods, too few fruits, vegetables and whole-grain breads and cereals, too much sugar and fat. It means a lack of necessary nutrients and fibre, as well as too many calories.

The unbalanced meals shown below are ones that many children might enjoy. They are fine for energy, protein and carbohydrates but are lacking in vitamins, minerals and fibre. This is because the eating pattern does not include enough milk, whole grain cereals, fruits and vegetables.

Unbalanced, Less-Healthy Meals	Balanced Healthy Meals
Breakfast	*Breakfast*
Cereal, high in sugar, low in fibre	Bran flakes
Milk	Milk
Orange Squash	Orange
Toast and jam	Toast and peanut butter
Lunch	*Lunch*
Hot dog, burger, jam or luncheon meat on white bread	Tuna fish or cheese sandwich on wholemeal bread
1 small bag of crisps	Raw carrots
4 chocolate biscuits	2 plain biscuits
Cola or lemonade	Apple
	Semi-skimmed milk
Dinner	*Dinner*
Fried chicken	Roast chicken
Chips	Baked potato
Roll with butter	Green beans
Strawberry Jelly	Fresh Fruit
Milk	Yogurt

Developing Good Eating Habits in Your Family

1. If you prepare good-tasting nutritious foods and don't let children snack too close to meal times, the rest is up to them. Don't nag, don't tell them that it is good for them or that other children around the world are starving — they couldn't care less. Make mealtimes enjoyable.

2. If you don't have crisps, sweets or fizzy drinks in the house, you won't have to argue with your children about whether or not they can have some. Healthy, nutritious food doesn't take long to prepare and young children like simple food best. What is faster for snacks than a banana, apple, carrot or yogurt?

3. Children will learn most from the example you set. If you don't like a certain food, there is a pretty good chance your

child won't either. If you snack on crisps just before dinner, so will your child.

4.   If children don't like a particular food or dish, try to work out why. Young children usually don't like hot, spicy food, mixtures of foods, sauces, or unfamiliar foods. Don't give up on new foods and don't make a fuss. Eventually they will be curious and want to try them. Sometimes young children will say they don't like a food because they are angry at you and they know this will upset you. Don't let a child's poor eating habits be attention-seekers and attention-getters.

For more information on feeding children you can refer to these two excellent books:

Cooking for Kids the Healthy Way by Joanna Pay (Dunitz).
Healthy Food for Kids by Carole Handslip (Sainsbury's Recipe Library.)

Feeding Your Teenager

The main challenge to feeding teenage boys is keeping enough food in the house. Concentrate on stocking wholesome foods rather than junk foods. Keep a large bowl of fruit out on the sideboard — they usually grab a banana or apple because they are there.

With teenage girls, eating problems are more complex and eating disorders such as anorexia nervosa are becoming distressingly prevalent. If you are worried about your daughter in this respect, don't hesitate to seek outside help from health professionals specializing in the field.

Iron and calcium deficiencies are common among teenagers, especially if they don't eat red meat or drink milk. Milk and milk products are the best sources of calcium. Most meats and meat alternates are good sources of iron. Many of the recipes in this book are high in calcium and/or iron. For example pizza is often a good source of calcium.

Here are some recipes with particular appeal to teenagers, which they may enjoy preparing. All of the recipes in this section are quick and easy to prepare and have been chosen with kids' preferences in mind. (See also menu and recipes for beginner cooks, pages 185–7.)

Mexican Beef Tacos or Tostadas

A tostada is a flat tortilla with toppings. A taco is a folded tortilla filled with a variety of foods such as grated cheese, shredded lettuce and meat sauce. Use this meat sauce as a basis for either and let each person top or fill his or her own taco or tostada

PER SERVING (made with 1 tbsp [15 ml] cheese)	
calories	295
g fat	14
g protein	19
g carbohydrate	24

Good: vitamin A, iron, fibre
Excellent: niacin

1 lb	lean minced beef	450
1	medium onion, chopped	
1	clove garlic, crushed	
3 oz	tomato purée	75
$\frac{1}{4}$ pt	water	150 m
2 tsp	chilli powder	10 m
1 tsp	dried oregano	5 m
$\frac{1}{2}$ tsp	cumin	2 m
$\frac{1}{4}$ tsp	hot red pepper flakes	1 m
	salt and freshly ground pepper	
16	6 in (15 cm) corn tortillas (tacos or tostadas)	1

Toppings

	shredded lettuce	
	chopped tomato	
	chopped green pepper	
	bottled or homemade taco sauce or Tomato Salsa Sauce (page 103)	
	yogurt	
	grated low-fat cheese	

Instead of bottled taco sauce, you can make your own by adding chopped fresh hot peppers or hot pepper sauce and dried hot pepper flakes to homemade tomato sauce. Alternatively, to keep the salt at a minimum, use Tomato Salsa, page 103, and add hot chillis to taste.

Keep the fat down by avoiding high-fat toppings. Avocado, or guacamole, is a popular taco topping, but avocado is extremely high in fat: 1 raw avocado has about 30 g of fat, nearly half the daily requirement of a woman.

In large pan, cook beef over medium heat until brown; pour off fat. Add onion and garlic; cook until tender. Stir in tomato purée, water, chilli powder, oregano, cumin and hot red peppe flakes. Simmer for 5 to 10 minutes. Taste and add salt, pepper, and hot pepper flakes to taste. (If mixture becomes dry, add a little water.) Spoon into serving dish.

Toppings: Place bowls of various toppings on table. Serve packaged crisp tortillas cold, or warm in 300°F (150°C) Gas Mark 2 oven for 5 minutes. Soft tortillas are usually fried in hot oil, but to keep fat content down, instead crisp them in a 400°F (200°C) Gas Mark 6 oven for 10 minutes.

To make tacos or tostadas, let each person spoon some meat mixture into tortilla then top with cheese, lettuce and other toppings of their choice. Makes 6 servings, 2 tacos each.

Compare	g fat	calories
Mexican Beef Tacos (2 tacos)	14	295
Mexican Beef Tacos or Tostadas with avocado, olives, Cheddar cheese toppings (2 tacos)	27	410

Vegetable Taco Sauce

Kidney beans make a tasty and nutritious change from meat in a taco or tostada filling. Add other seasonal vegetables, such as chopped courgettes, broccoli, peppers or sweet corn, that you might have on hand. Use the same toppings and procedure as in Mexican Beef Tacos or Tostadas.

2 tsp	vegetable oil	10 ml
2	onions, chopped	2
1	clove garlic, crushed	1
2	carrots, finely chopped	2
2	tomatoes, chopped	2
1	can (19 oz [540 ml]) red kidney beans, drained	1
1	green chilli (canned or fresh), chopped (optional)	1
2 tsp	chilli powder	10 ml
1 tsp	cumin	5 ml
$\frac{1}{4}$ tsp	hot red pepper flakes	1 ml
	salt and freshly ground pepper	

In large nonstick saucepan, heat oil over medium heat; add onions, garlic and carrots and cook for 5 minutes or until tender, stirring often. Add tomatoes, beans, green chilli (if using), chilli powder, cumin and hot pepper flakes. Season to taste with salt, pepper, and more hot pepper flakes, if desired.

Simmer, uncovered, for 15 to 20 minutes or until sauce is thickened and flavours blended. Makes enough for 12 tacos, along with other toppings.

ariation
stead of taco shells serve
getable Taco Sauce over
asted wholemeal bread or
mburger buns.

utrition note
reduce the salt content use
rn tortillas instead of
mmercial taco shells or
stadas.

PER SERVING (of sauce plus 2 taco shells)	
calories	168
g fat	5
g protein	5
g carbohydrate	26
Good: vitamin C	
Excellent: fibre, vitamin A, niacin	

PER 2-PIECE SERVING	
calories	424
g fat	16
g protein	25
g carbohydrate	46
Good: riboflavin, vitamin A, iron	
Excellent: fibre, vitamin C, thiamin, niacin, calcium	

Nutritious Pizza
Good-tasting pizza can also be very nutritious. If you choose vegetables such as broccoli, onion, peppers, tomatoes, courgettes, mushrooms and reduced-fat cheese for toppings, your pizza will be a good source of calcium, vitamins A and C, and fibre.

If, instead, you choose anchovies, olives, pepperoni, and mozzarella or cheddar cheese, you will double the fat and salt. The pizza will still be a good source of calcium but it will be too low in fibre and vitamins.

If your children don't like broccoli, don't assume they won't like it on pizza. They might be receptive to it in this way.

One serving (2 pieces) of Mushroom, Broccoli and Onion Pizza provides the following percentage of daily recommended intake: protein 42%, vitamin A 22%, vitamin C 65%, thiamin 33%, riboflavin 40%, niacin 45%, calcium 50%, iron 22%.

Mushroom, Broccoli and Onion Pizza

Keep some homemade or store-bought pizza dough rounds in your freezer so you can easily make your own fast food. Depending on the toppings you choose, your pizzas can be nutritious as well as delicious. (Recipe pictured opposite page 185.)

1	round (12 in [30 cm]) pizza base	
4 oz	chopped tomatoes	100
1 tsp	dried oregano (or 2 tbsp [30 ml] fresh)	5 n
$\frac{1}{2}$ tsp	dried basil (or 1 tbsp [15 ml] fresh)	2 n
10	mushrooms, sliced	1
1 lb	small broccoli florets	450
1	small onion, thinly sliced	
$\frac{1}{2}$	red and/or yellow pepper, chopped	
10 oz	shredded low-fat cheese	250

Place pizza base on baking sheet. Combine tomato sauce, oregano and basil; mix well and spread over pizza base. Arrange mushrooms, broccoli, onion and yellow pepper on top Sprinkle with cheese. Bake in 475°F (240°C) Gas Mark 9 oven for 12 minutes or until cheese is bubbling. Cut into 8 pieces. Makes 4 servings (2 pieces each).

Compare (2 pieces)	g fat	calories
Pizza in this book	16	424
Normal homemade pizza (made with mozzarella, pepperoni, anchovies, green olives)	29	541

Feeding a Family on the Run

Today every family has a busy schedule. Mothers who work outside the home and single parents are particularly hard-pressed to find the time and energy to make meals. Once you get in the habit, though, you'll find it is not difficult to make a delicious and healthy meal for four in 30 minutes, if you have the ingredients in the house. Here are some tips for mealtimes in busy households:

*If getting a meal on the table is a problem, discuss meal planning with the whole family and try to divide up the jobs, from shopping to putting groceries away to cooking and cleaning up. Younger family members like to help and they can set the table, peel carrots, wash lettuce — don't worry about the mess, they eventually get tidier.

Don't give up if you meet some resistance. In our house, every year — sometimes every month — we come up with new ways to divide the jobs. We have just started a system in which each person makes dinner one night a week. Even if it only lasts for two weeks it's worth it to me.

*Cook extra on the weekends: double whatever you make on Saturday and Sunday and eat it again during the week. Many of the recipes in the book are suitable for reheating or can be eaten cold throughout the week: Simple Beef and Vegetable Stew (page 72); Split Pea, Bean and Barley Soup (page 43); Chunky Vegetable and Bean Soup (page 35); Mexican Rice and Bean Casserole (page 114); Beef and Pasta Casserole (page 74); Pasta and Fresh Vegetable Salad (page 59). Or, cook a number of vegetables and a large roast, chicken or turkey on Sunday, then on Monday have it cold and reheat the vegetables. On Tuesday use the meat in a casserole or soup.

*Do a little meal preparation before you go out in the morning; for example, chop up meat for a stir-fry (page 69), or get a chicken out of the freezer and leave a note or make arrangements for someone else in the family to put it in the oven at a certain time.

*Hire someone to do some cooking as an alternative to fast foods, eating out and using many prepared foods. If you are constantly eating meals at fast-food chains or using prepared and convenience foods (which are usually high in fat and salt and low in fibre), examine the reasons why and consider alternatives.

It might not be any more expensive to hire someone to do some cooking for you: a student, a cleaning lady, your own child or your housekeeper. This person could help you on a regular basis either daily, weekly or monthly — or just occasionally. Consider spending an evening cooking with the fill-in chef and show him or her how to make a few of your favourite dishes, or prepare some of the recipes in this book. When I'm really under pressure at work, I hire someone to make huge quantities of All-Purpose Quick Spaghetti Sauce (see below) and freeze it in 1–2 pt ($\frac{1}{2}$–1 lit) containers. I then use it as a base for chilli, tacos, casseroles and lasagne, as well as spaghetti.

Recipes for Family Suppers

Here are some quick and easy solutions to last-minute meal preparation.

All-Purpose Quick Spaghetti Sauce

I make this sauce in large amounts then freeze it in 1 pt (600 ml) containers. You can double or triple this recipe. Sometimes I add chopped carrot, green pepper, celery or mushrooms. My children like it best over spaghetti noodles sprinkled with Parmesan cheese. It's also good as a base for lasagne, tacos, chilli or casseroles.

1 lb	minced beef	450
2	onions, chopped	
1	large clove garlic, crushed	
1	can (5$\frac{1}{2}$ oz [156 g]) tomato purée	
1	can (28 oz [796 g]) tomatoes (or 16 fl oz [500 ml] water)	
1 tsp	dried oregano	5 m
1 tsp	dried basil	5 m
$\frac{1}{2}$ tsp	dried thyme	2 m
$\frac{1}{4}$ tsp	freshly ground pepper	1 m

In large heavy pan, cook beef over medium heat until no longer pink, breaking up with spoon. Pour off fat. Stir in onion and garlic; cook until softened. Stir in tomato purée, tomatoes (breaking up with back of spoon), oregano, basil, thyme and pepper.

Bring to boil, reduce heat and simmer for 10 minutes; thin with water if desired. Taste and adjust seasonings if necessary. Makes 6 servings.

PER SERVING	
calories	195
g fat	9
g protein	17
g carbohydrate	14

Good: fibre, vitamin A
Excellent: vitamin C, niacin, iron

Quick Chilli
In saucepan, combine 16 fl oz (500 ml) All-Purpose Quick Spaghetti Sauce, one 19 oz (540 g) can each kidney beans (drained) and beans with sausages, and 1 tbsp (15 ml) chilli powder.

Bring to a simmer over medium heat, stirring occasionally. Add chilli powder and hot pepper flakes to taste.

Last-Minute Pasta Casserole

This is another of my children's favourites. If there are any leftovers, my son John heats them up in the microwave for breakfast or snacks. It's a good dish for small children who don't like to chew meat. I never seem to make this exactly the same way twice, and I add what vegetables I have on hand: fresh tomatoes and courgettes in the summer, celery and carrots in the winter. Add fresh basil if you have it.

4 oz	macaroni or shell pasta	100 g
16 fl oz	All-Purpose Quick Spaghetti Sauce (p. 182)	500 ml
1	small green or yellow pepper, chopped	1
4	large mushrooms, sliced	4
5 oz	sweetcorn or green peas	130 g
2 tbsp	grated Parmesan cheese	30 ml

In large pan of boiling water, cook macaroni until al dente (tender but firm); drain.

Meanwhile, in flameproof casserole or heavy saucepan over medium heat, combine Spaghetti Sauce, pepper, mushrooms and sweetcorn or peas; simmer for 5 minutes. Stir in hot cooked pasta; sprinkle each serving with Parmesan cheese. Makes 4 servings.

PER SERVING	
calories	247
g fat	5
g protein	14
g carbohydrate	37

Good: fibre, iron
Excellent: vitamin C, niacin

Stocking the Basics

Sometimes we eat out at food chains or order a takeaway because we don't have the ingredients in the house to make a fast meal. There are a few simple tips for always having the makings of a fast, healthy meal at home.

Keep your kitchen stocked with staple foods, such as whole-wheat pastas, cereals, rice, tomato purée, canned beans, tuna, salmon, peanut butter and low-fat yogurt. Keep wholemeal pitta bread, peas, sweetcorn, and juice in your freezer, along with chicken and fish fillets.

Vegetables such as cabbage, cauliflower, turnip, cucumber, and carrots, and reduced-fat cheeses and eggs will keep for three to four weeks in the refrigerator.

Below are a few recipes for which you can keep the ingredients on your shelf or in the freezer. Even when the refrigerator looks bare you'll still be able to make these nutritious dishes.

Linguine with Salmon and Chives (page 99)
Fish Fillets with Basil and Lemon (page 95)
Herb-Breaded Fish Fillets (page 94)
Barbecued Lemon Chicken (page 81)
Herb-Breaded Chicken (page 189)
Bean Casserole with Tomatoes and Spinach (page 106)
Mexican Rice and Bean Casserole (page 114)

Macaroni with Tomato and Tuna Sauce

You'll probably have all the ingredients for this popular economical family dish right in your own cupboard. My children gobble it up and, at first, didn't know if it was tuna or chicken in the sauce.

PER SERVING	
calories	328
g fat	4
g protein	23
g carbohydrate	49
Good: fibre, iron	
Excellent: vitamin C, niacin	

1 tbsp	olive oil	15 m
1	small onion, chopped	1
1	clove garlic, crushed	1
1	can (14 oz [398 g]) tomatoes	1
4 fl oz	chicken stock	125 m
1 tsp	dried basil (or 2 tbsp [30 ml] chopped fresh)	5 m
½ tsp	dried rosemary (or 2 tsp [10 ml] fresh)	2 m
1	tin (7 oz [198 g]) tuna, drained	1
	salt and freshly ground pepper	
½ oz	chopped fresh parsley (optional)	15 g
½ lb	macaroni or penne	225 g

Right:
Streusel Plum Cake (page 160)

In heavy saucepan, heat oil over medium heat; cook onion and garlic for 5 minutes or until tender, stirring occasionally.

Add tomatoes and break up using back of spoon. Stir in chicken stock, basil and rosemary; simmer, uncovered, for 10 minutes. Stir in tuna and simmer for 5 minutes. Season with salt and pepper to taste; add parsley (if using).

Meanwhile, in large pan of boiling water, cook macaroni until al dente (tender but firm); drain. Toss with tomato mixture and serve immediately. Makes 4 servings.

The Beginner Cook

Often we get tied up at work and can't get home or are just too tired at the end of a day to make a meal. Instead of ordering in a pizza, here are some suggestions for meals that teenagers or a beginner cook can make for themselves or for the family.
- Hamburger, raw carrots, milk, apple or pear
- Canned baked beans in tomato sauce, green pepper strips, wholemeal bread, milk, banana
- Scrambled eggs, peas, salad, toast, milk, sorbet and biscuit
- Roast chicken, baked potatoes, any frozen vegetables (or fresh if they know how to prepare and cook them), or salad, milk, fresh or canned fruit in natural juice.

Recipes for the Beginner Cook

One of the most difficult tasks for young cooks is to have everything ready at once. It's a good idea to choose a menu with one or two cold dishes, or foods for which timing isn't critical. Try this one.
Hamburgers
Oven-Baked French Fries (page 186)
Red and Green Cabbage Slaw (page 186)
Microwave Oatmeal Squares (page 187)
Frozen Strawberry Yogurt (page 187)

ft:
ushroom, Broccoli and
nion Pizza (page 180)

Oven-Baked French Fries

These good-tasting chips are much healthier and easier to make than the ones that you deep-fry in fat.

PER SERVING	
calories	179
g fat	3
g protein	3
g carbohydrate	35
Good: fibre, niacin, iron	
Excellent: vitamin C	

4	medium potatoes (1½ lb [665 g])	
1 tbsp	vegetable oil	15 m
	paprika	
	grated Parmesan cheese (optional)	

   Wash potatoes but don't peel; slice into ½ in (1 cm) thick strips. Toss potatoes with oil in a bowl until coated; sprinkle with paprika. Spread on baking sheet and bake in 475°F (240°C) Ga Mark 9 oven for 25 to 30 minutes, or until golden, turning occasionally.
   Toss with Parmesan (if using). Makes 4 servings.

Red and Green Cabbage Slaw

This colourful, easy-to-make salad goes well with hamburgers, toasted cheese sandwiches and many summer picnic or barbecue menus. If red cabbage is hard to find, use only green cabbage and add 1 or 2 shredded carrots. Chopped red or gree pepper, celery, courgettes, onion, apple or raisins are nice additions.

PER SERVING	
calories	49
g fat	4
g protein	1
g carbohydrate	4
Good: fibre	
Excellent: vitamin C	

6 oz	shredded green cabbage	150
6 oz	shredded red cabbage	150
2 oz	chopped spring onion	50
2 oz	low-fat mayonnaise	50
2 oz	low-fat natural yogurt	50
1 oz	chopped fresh parsley	25
	salt and freshly ground pepper	

   In salad bowl, combine green and red cabbage, onion, mayonnaise, yogurt, parsley, and salt and pepper to taste. Mix well, cover and refrigerate for up to 4 hours. Makes 6 serving

Microwave Oatmeal Squares

These are very easy and the fastest squares I know how to make.
Use any crumbs left in the pan with yogurt as a topping over
fruit.

2 oz	unsaturated margarine	50 g
$\frac{1}{2}$ tsp	almond or vanilla essence	2 ml
2 oz	packed brown sugar	50 g
8 oz	rolled oats	225 g

In 8 in (2 lit) square glass or microwave-safe dish, microwave
margarine at high (100%) power for 40 to 60 seconds or until
melted. Stir in extract and sugar; mix well. Stir in rolled oats; mix
well.

Firmly press mixture into pan. Microwave at high (100%)
power for 5 minutes. Let cool and cut into 25 squares.

To Bake in Conventional Oven
Melt margarine, combine with extract and sugar, then add oats;
mix well. Press into pan; bake in 350°F (180°C) Gas Mark 4
oven for 15 minutes or until bubbling and golden brown.

PER SQUARE

alories	71
fat	4
protein	1
carbohydrate	8

Frozen Strawberry Yogurt

Creamy and full of flavour, this frozen dessert is a refreshing
finale to any meal and a favourite of my daughter Susie. In
strawberry season serve with fresh strawberries and a biscuit.

$\frac{1}{2}$ lb	strawberries or 1 pkg (10 oz [300 g]) frozen, thawed	225 g
9 oz	low-fat natural yogurt	230 g
1 oz	icing sugar	25 g
1 tbsp	lemon juice	15 ml

In food processor or blender, purée strawberries; you should
have about 10 oz (250 g). Add yogurt, sugar and lemon juice,
process for 1 second or until mixed.

Pour into metal bowl or ice cream machine and freeze
according to instructions on page 165. Makes 5 servings.

PER SERVING

calories	81
fat	1
protein	3
carbohydrate	17
Excellent: vitamin C	

Fast Food At Home

Instead of ordering a takeaway pizza or chicken, here are a few tasty and healthy alternatives.

20-Minute Home-Cooked Chicken Dinner for Four

per serving	g fat	calories
Herb Breaded Chicken (page 189)	3	162
Rice (4 oz [100 g])	—	80
Peas with Spring Onions (page 120)	2	68
Sliced tomato ($\frac{1}{2}$)	—	12
Semi-skimmed milk ($\frac{1}{2}$ pt [300 ml])	5	128
Total Calories from fat = 20%	10	450
Total with 2 pieces chicken	13	612

Compare this with:

Kentucky Fried Chicken Dinner*

per serving	g fat	calories
1 piece side breast per person 3$\frac{1}{2}$ oz (90 g)	17	276
French fries 4 oz (100 g)	13	268
Coleslaw 3 oz (75 g)	6	105
Semi-skimmed milk ($\frac{1}{2}$ pt [300 ml])	5	128
Total Calories from fat = 47%	41	777
Total with 2 pieces of chicken	58	1053

*Six pieces of Kentucky Nuggets have about the same amount of fat (17 g) as one piece of Kentucky Fried breast meat.

Frozen, Precooked Chicken Breast Dinner**	g fat	calories
11 oz (280 g) portion (chicken, potatoes, sweetcorn, sugar, margarine, eggs, salt, monosodium glutamate, butter)	32	650
Semi-skimmed milk ($\frac{1}{2}$ pt [300 ml])	5	128
Total Calories from fat = 43%	37	778

**This is a smaller portion than the above two dinners. Frozen dinners vary considerably in their content; read the label carefully.

Herb-Breaded Chicken

My son John likes to make this when it is his turn to cook dinner. I try to keep chicken breasts and a jar of these seasoned bread crumbs in my freezer so I can make this in a jiffy. Don't worry if you don't have all the herbs, just use a little more of the ones you have. I also use these crumbs on pork tenderloin, fish fillets and grilled tomato halves.

$1\frac{1}{2}$	slices wholemeal bread	$1\frac{1}{2}$
$\frac{1}{4}$ tsp	each dried basil, thyme, oregano, tarragon, paprika and salt	1 ml
	freshly ground pepper	
1 lb	boneless skinless chicken breasts (about 4 breast pieces) (or 2 lb [1 kg] bone-in chicken breasts*)	450 g

In food processor or blender, process bread to make crumbs. Add basil, thyme, oregano, tarragon, paprika, salt, and pepper to taste; process to mix.

Rinse chicken under cold running water; shake off water. Transfer crumb mixture to plastic bag; add chicken a few pieces at a time and shake to coat.

Place chicken in single layer in microwave-safe dish or on baking sheet. Bake in 400°F (200°C) Gas Mark 6 oven for 18 to 20 minutes for boneless breasts, 40 minutes for bone-in or until no longer pink inside.

Microwave Method
Microwave, uncovered, at high (100%) power for 5 minutes for boneless, 9 minutes for bone-in; let stand for 1 minute. Makes 4 servings.

---

*When using bone-in chicken breasts, double the amount of bread and herbs.

ngle Serving

r one boneless chicken east, use about $\frac{2}{3}$ oz (20 g) of umb mixture (freeze maining for another time). ke or microwave, ncovered, on high power for minutes; let stand for 1 inute.

lways use the leaf form of ied herbs, not the wdered, and find most cipes are better with this rm. Also, the more finely ound the herbs the quicker ey will lose flavour under orage.

PER SERVING	
calories	162
g fat	3
g protein	26
g carbohydrate	6

ther quick-to-make chicken cipes

rbecued Lemon Chicken age 81)
rilled Turkey Escalopes with erbs and Garlic (page 92)
ir-Fried Chicken with occoli (page 89)

Compare Home-Cooked and Fast-Food Hamburgers

Home-Cooked Hamburger Dinner	g fat	calorie
Hamburger (medium grilled) includes bun	18	404
Pickle relish (1 tbsp [15 ml])	0	21
Lettuce, onions, tomatoes	0	8
Raw carrot (1)	0	31
Semi-skimmed milk ($\frac{1}{2}$ pt [300 ml])	5	128
Total	23	592

McDonald's Hamburger Dinner		
Quarter Pounder (160 g)	24	427
Small french fries (68 g)	12	220
Vanilla shake (10.2 oz [291 g])	8	352
Total	44	999
Total with semi-skimmed milk (no shake)	41	775
Total with Big Mac instead of Quarter Pounder	52	918

NOTE: The most notable difference between home-cooked and fast-food hamburgers is their salt content. The extra fat and calories in a McDonald's meal come from the fries and shake. *If you eat at a fast-food burger chain, omit the fries, choose skimmed or semi-skimmed milk, and make a salad from the salad bar using only a small amount o dressing.*

Frozen Hamburger Patties

Until I was assigned an article on using frozen hamburger patties for *Canadian Living's Food* magazine, I didn't realize what a convenience it would be to have these on hand. It doesn't take long to make hamburger patties, and they are much easier to use than a block of frozen meat. Lean ground pork or lamb also make tasty patties, and they can be combined with beef.

4 lb	lean minced beef	2 kg
3	onions, finely chopped	3
1	green pepper, finely chopped (optional)	1
1	egg	1
1 tsp	dry mustard	5 ml
1 tsp	Worcestershire sauce	5 ml
½ tsp	freshly ground pepper	2 ml
Dash	hot pepper sauce	Dash

In large bowl, combine beef, onions, green pepper (if using), egg, mustard, Worcestershire sauce, pepper and hot pepper sauce; with spoon or hands, mix just until combined.

Using ice-cream scoop or hands, divide mixture into 20 portions; shape each portion into round patty. Place patties on baking sheets and freeze until solid, 4 to 5 hours. Stack patties with foil or paper plates between them. Package in freezer bags and store up to 4 months in freezer. Makes 20 patties.

PER PATTY

calories	169
g fat	10
g protein	17
g carbohydrate	1

Good: iron
Excellent: niacin

grill, place frozen patties on grill 3 to 4 in (8 to 10 cm) from grill. Cook for about 5 minutes on each side or until browned and to preference.

PER SERVING	
calories	357
g fat	13
g protein	28
g carbohydrate	36
Good: fibre, vitamin C, thiamin, riboflavin, calcium, iron	
Excellent: niacin	

Best Tzatziki

If you have time to make tzatziki in advance, use this method for a longer lasting thicker texture. Line a sieve with cheesecloth or muslin; add yogurt and let drain for 2 to 4 hours. Place chopped cucumber in a colander and sprinkle with ¼ tsp (1 ml) salt, let stand for 30 minutes then rinse under cold water and pat dry. Combine drained yogurt, cucumber and garlic; mix well. Cover and refrigerate up to 2 days.

Middle-Eastern Patties

For a nice change, try beef or lamb patties in wholemeal pitta bread pockets topped with garlicky Greek Tzatziki which is so delicious any extra can be used as a dip with pitta bread.

4	hamburger patties
4	wholemeal pitta rounds (6 in [15 cm])
	shredded lettuce

Quick Tzatziki

9 oz	low-fat natural yogurt or fromage frais	230
½	cucumber, peeled and finely chopped or grated	
1	large clove garlic, crushed	

Quick Tzatziki: In small bowl, combine yogurt, cucumber and garlic; mix well.

Grill hamburger patties to desired doneness. Cut slice off each pitta bread about 1 in (2.5 cm) from edge; pull apart to form opening. Heat pittas in microwave or oven until warm. Place hot hamburger patty and shredded lettuce inside pitta; spoon about ⅓ oz (12 g) Tzatziki over each hamburger. Makes 4 servings.

Fast Foods and Takeaways

Grabbing a quick bite on the way home from work or ordering takeaway pizza is part of today's lifestyle. Since these foods are often high in fat and salt but adequate in protein, the other food or meals you eat at home should be low in fat and high in vitamins and fibre. If your dieting daughter eats lunch at fast-food chains and often has a hamburger for lunch, she can balance it out with homemade soup, raw vegetables, bread and an apple for dinner. The following table offers some excellent suggestions for making a fast-food meal more nutritious.

Takeaway	Nutritional Considerations	Nutrient Boosters
Hamburgers	• choose grilled or barbecued hamburgers • don't have mayonnaise, sauce or chips • usually low in vitamins A, C, calcium and fibre	• stay away from the mayonnaise and choose lots of lettuce and tomatoes for added vitamins A and C • choose a salad for added fibre • ask for a wholemeal bun • add a glass of skimmed or semi-skimmed milk to your meal for calcium and/or have a cheeseburger — you'll boost your calcium even more • try a vegetable or beanburger for a change, its lower on fat
Fish and Chips	• very high in fat and calories • some calcium in the batter flour and vitamin C (from potatoes) • enjoy only as an occasional treat	• ask whether they fry in an unsaturated oil or animal fat and choose a place that uses oils if possible • share a portion of fish with a friend • choose fish cooked in breadcrumbs rather than batter if possible
Pizza	• order a cheese and vegetable pizza, leave off the ham, bacon and pepperoni — these are high in fat and salt • lots of calcium here, but low in vitamins A, C, iron and fibre	• start with a spinach/orange salad and finish with some fruit for added fibre • some pizza parlours offer wholemeal base — ask when you order • choose a mixed salad to accompany it — or share one with a friend • avoid high fat dressings — crispy bacon bits, croutons, avocado
Chicken	• choose barbecued, baked or grilled • remove the skin, don't have sauce/gravy, or chips • low in vitamins A and C, iron and fibre	• add a wholemeal bun, glass of skimmed or semi-skimmed milk and a salad • choose a baked potato for added nutrients and fibre • don't have the butter and sour cream
Kebabs	• cubed lamb or pork in a pitta bread with tomatoes and yogurt/garlic sauce • low in vitamins A, C, calcium and fibre	• extra tomatoes boost the vitamin A and C • for added fibre and calcium, choose wholemeal pitta bread and a glass of skimmed or semi-skimmed milk
Chinese	• high in salt and MSG • choose stir-fried dishes, include a vegetable dish and steamed rice • low in calcium and vitamin C	• boost vitamin C — include a dish with broccoli or Chinese greens • add skimmed or semi-skimmed milk to your meal or try a tofu stir-fry. You can even catch up on your calcium later in the day • Chow mein (includes noodles) and Chop Suey (includes bean sprouts) are relatively low in fat
Tacos	• high in fat • low in vitamins A, C and calcium	• have a glass of skimmed or semi-skimmed milk and fruit for dessert • try a bean or chicken taco for less fat and lots of iron; bean tacos also provide fibre
Indian	• ask how dishes are cooked (many have hidden fats, some are surprisingly low) • boiled rice is low in fat • yogurt-based dips and spicy pickles, give flavour without fat	• lentil and pulse dishes (e.g. dahl) are very high in fibre • Tandoori is low in fat • Chapatti is low but Naan bread very high in fat
Baked potato	• lots of fibre in potato skin • high vitamin C and iron content in the potato • avoid high fat toppings and fillings (e.g.) butter, cheese, creamy sauces; choose low fat (e.g.) baked beans, vegetable chilli/curry	• check they don't automatically serve it with butter • use pickle or sauce for moisture without the fat • ask for a glass of skimmed or semi-skimmed milk and/or a side salad for even more nourishment
Delicattessan	• bear in mind that products looking or declaring to be 'pure, natural and wholesome' may be made with 'natural ingredients' but could be much higher in fat than you'd imagine • avoid deep-fried products (e.g.) samosas. Even vegetarian ones can contain over 80% calories from fat!	• ask for more information about ingredients and methods of preparation and cooking • read the labels and compare the amount of fat per 100 g or per serving

Eating Out and Travelling

Recent studies have shown that lifestyle is the important factor in determining how healthily you eat. Men and women who travel and eat out frequently tend to be more likely to have a high-fat diet than those who don't travel.

If you only eat out for special occasions or once a month, enjoy your meal and order what you want. If, however, you eat out often it's important to make nutritious menu choices. Too often we eat more than we would at home, more high-fat foods and not enough fruits and vegetables.

Tips for Healthy Restaurant Eating
* Choose a restaurant where you can make nutritious choices such as salads, soups, vegetables and fruits. Some restaurants mark low-fat dishes on the menu.
* Have a glass of water as soon as you are seated in order to control your urge to eat, as well as to ensure you get enough fluids.
* Avoid buffets and all-you-can-eat specials if you tend to overeat.
* Order salad dressings and sauces on the side and add only a small amount.
* Ask for vegetables served without butter.
* If you eat the breads and rolls, pass on the butter or ask for a low-fat spread.
* Avoid gravies and sauces made with cream and butter.
* Avoid fried, sautéed and deep-fried foods; instead, choose grilled, poached, baked, roasted or boiled dishes.
* Trim all visible fat from meat, skin from poultry.
* Choose chicken or fish; avoid duck and goose.
* Choose baked potato rather than chips. Avoid butter and go easy on the sour cream, or choose yogurt instead.
* Ask for extra vegetables and small portions of meat.
* If you have dessert, order fresh fruit or sorbet, avoid pastries and whipped-cream desserts.
* Don't feel you have to eat everything on your plate because you are paying for it. Some restaurant portions are very large and can easily be shared.
* Avoid nondairy creamer, which is high in saturated fat; for coffee or tea choose milk instead.
* If a restaurant or hotel room-service menu doesn't offer many healthy choices, make a special request. They are in the business to please; if enough people ask for nutritious dishes, they might change their menus.
* Try a vegetarian choice; unless in pastry or a rich creamy sauce, it is likely to be lower in fat and calories.

Healthy Breakfast	g fat	calories	Less Healthy Breakfast	g fat	calories
Orange or fresh fruit	trace	62	Croissant	12	235
Whole-grain cereal	trace	95	Fried eggs (2) and bacon (2 slices)	18	241
Yogurt or milk, skimmed	trace	90	Coffee with cream	3	28
Healthy Lunch			**Less Healthy Lunch**		
Spinach salad (minimum dressing)	7	93	Cream soup	14	215
Pasta with tomato-based sauce and Parmesan cheese	11	368	Quiche	48	600
Raspberry sorbet	0	109	Chocolate pudding	10	191
Healthy Dinner			**Less Healthy Dinner**		
Consommé with vegetables	3	91	Pâté	5	59
Most fish or chicken dishes (4 oz [100 g]) (easy on the sauce)	4	148	12 oz (300 g) steak	36	752
Rice (4 oz [100 g]) or potato (no butter and not fried)	trace	101	Potato (with butter) or chips (10)	8	158
Asparagus or green beans	trace	15	Tossed salad	trace	11
with lemon and 1 tsp (5 ml) margarine	4	33	with 2 tbsp (30 ml) Thousand Island dressing	12	128
Fresh strawberries, 8 oz (225 g)	trace	47	Strawberry cheesecake	8	222
Total	29	1252		174	2840
Calories from fat = 21%			Calories from fat = 55%		

Note: For healthy meals, to gain calories choose larger portions and nutritious snacks. The British Heart Foundation recommends not more than 35% of calories should come from fat per day.

Cooking for One

When I lived by myself I would come home from work, open the refrigerator and start to eat. Unless I invited someone for dinner, I lived on cheese and crackers, scrambled eggs, sandwiches, soups, raw vegetables and fruit. This diet can be nutritious but it does become boring. Because sometimes I didn't even bother to put the food on a plate but would eat on the run, I ate more than I needed and gained weight. Finding the motivation to cook and learning how to shop for one are the two key problems confronting people who live alone.

It's difficult to discuss cooking for one or two in a few pages because people's eating patterns vary widely. A single 22-year-old male's nutritional requirements and eating preferences will be different from those of a 70-year-old widow. Following the Food Guide (page 206) and eating foods from the four main food groups each day is an easy way to ensure that everyone eats healthily.

Tips for Shopping and Cooking for One

* Shop at a place where you can buy small portions and everything isn't pre-packaged.
* When possible, buy only what you can use. It's more economical to buy a small can and use it all than to buy a larger size and throw half away.
* When you can't buy a small portion of a vegetable, think up different ways to use it. For example, use broccoli in a salad, soup, omelet, stir-fry, over pasta, with cheese or just simply boiled.
* The microwave oven is an advantage not only for speed, but it means you don't have to warm up a large oven to cook or reheat a small portion. A toaster oven is also great for reheating small portions.
* If you eat out often at lunch, make it your main meal of the day; you will only need to prepare a light meal in the evening
* Because you don't have to buy large amounts you can treat yourself to special foods and more expensive foods, such as an out-of-season vegetable or a punnet of strawberries, or a salmon steak.
* Many of the recipes (such as the pasta dishes) in this book are for four servings. You can easily have them and either freeze one portion or refrigerate the leftovers and use the next day

Nutrition for the Elderly

Many people who live alone are also older and have some special nutritional needs. For the elderly, energy or calorie needs are often less but nutrient needs are not. This means that the foods that older people eat should be high in nutrients and that there isn't much room for empty-calorie foods, such as sweets, and alcohol. Most communities have a Meals-on-Wheels service for elderly people who have trouble shopping and preparing food for themselves. Make sure the elderly people you care about aren't making do with tea and toast.

* Fatigue and apathy can be the result of poor nutrition, especially too little protein and iron.
* Complex carbohydrates and fibre-rich foods such as fruits, vegetables, wholemeal breads and cereals should be emphasized.
* Some medications, either prescription or over-the-counter drugs and laxatives, can cause vitamin and mineral deficiencies. Consult your doctor about whether you need a vitamin-mineral supplement.
* As you get older your taste buds and thirst signals aren't as strong. It's important to drink six to eight glasses of fluids and not to oversalt foods.

Recipes for One

The following two recipes for Sole with Tomatoes and Stir-Fry for One are simple and quick. The trick is always to keep such basic ingredients as tomato purée, oil, lemon and seasonings in your cupboard so that you can prepare meals at short notice.

Chicken for One

See Herb-Breaded Chicken
(page 189)

PER SERVING (with chicken)	
calories	292
g fat	13
g protein	31
g carbohydrate	15
Good: iron	
Excellent: vitamin C, fibre, niacin, vitamin A	

Stir-Fry for One

Stir-fries are a quick and easy meal for one or two people and an excellent way to use up a piece of broccoli or half a red pepper lurking in the refrigerator — add a few more vegetables and they can easily be stretched to make an extra serving. Don't be put off by the long list of ingredients — they only take a minute or two to put together and taste delicious. Serve over hot rice or noodles.

¼ lb	boneless chicken, beef, or pork	100 g
1 tsp	cornflour	5 ml
1 tbsp	sherry or white wine	15 ml
1	stalk broccoli or celery or ½ pepper	
2 tsp	vegetable oil	10 ml
1	clove garlic, crushed	
1 tsp	fresh root ginger, grated	5 ml
Seasoning sauce		
1 tbsp	water	15 ml
1 tbsp	sherry or white wine	15 ml
½ tsp	cornflour	2 ml
½ tsp	soy sauce	2 ml

Cut meat into very thin strips about 2 in (5 cm) long. In bowl, mix cornflour and sherry; stir in meat and let stand for 10 minutes or up to 2 hours. Cut vegetables into thin strips or florets. In small bowl, combine seasoning sauce ingredients and mix well.

In wok or non-stick pan, heat oil over high heat. Add garlic, ginger and meat and stir-fry for 1 minute. Add broccoli or other vegetable and stir-fry 2 minutes or until crisp tender; add water if necessary to prevent scorching. Stir in seasoning sauce and stir-fry for another minute. Makes 1 serving.

Sole with Tomatoes

This is an absolutely delicious and easy-to-make dish for one.
Serve with a green vegetable along with potatoes, rice or bread.
For two servings, double the ingredients and place on one plate
before microwaving for 4 to 5 minutes.

1	medium tomato, thickly sliced	1
1	fillet sole, about 5 oz (125 g)	1
$\frac{1}{2}$ tsp	olive oil	2 ml
$\frac{1}{2}$ tsp	lemon juice	2 ml
2 tsp	chopped fresh basil, dill or parsley (or $\frac{1}{4}$ tsp [1 ml] dried)	10 ml
	freshly ground pepper	

PER SERVING	
calories	141
g fat	4
g protein	22
g carbohydrate	6
Good: fibre, vitamin A	
Excellent: vitamin C, niacin	

On microwave-safe plate, arrange tomato slices in single
layer. Arrange fish to cover tomatoes; drizzle with oil and lemon
juice. Sprinkle with basil, and pepper to taste. Cover and
microwave at high (100%) power for 3 minutes or until fish is
almost opaque and flakes easily when tested with fork. Remove
from oven and let stand for 1 minute. If necessary, pour off
excess liquid from plate. Makes 1 serving.

Conventional Oven Method
In shallow baking dish arrange fish; cover with sliced tomato.
Drizzle with oil and lemon juice. Sprinkle with basil and pepper
to taste. Bake in 400°F (200°C) Gas Mark 6 oven for 12 minutes
or until fish is almost opaque and flakes easily when tested with
a fork.

Shopping

The shop or supermarket is the first place to start thinking about
healthy eating. It doesn't matter how well you cook if you
haven't bought the right foods in the first place. Some of the
new products on the shelves make it much easier to cook in a
fast and healthy way than it was 30 years ago, but the opposite
can also be true. Spend a few minutes reading labels, especially
the first time you buy a new product or brand. As a rule, the
more processed or prepared the food, the fewer nutrients and
the more fat, sugar and salt it contains.

Choose	Avoid (or choose less often)
Milk and Milk Products	
Skimmed or semi-skimmed milk	Whole milk
Natural low-fat or diet yogurt	Whole milk yogurt
Cottage cheese	
Low-fat cheeses, (i.e) mozzarella, ricotta cheese, feta, Camembert, Edam, Brie, low-fat cream cheeses	Use less of high-fat cheese, such as Cheddar, Stilton, Danish Blue
Fromage frais	Cream, sour cream
Meat, Fish, Poultry	
Lean cuts of beef — round, rump; medium and lean minced beef	Fatty cuts — prime rib, fatty minced beef, bacon, spareribs
Fish	
Chicken, turkey (without skin)	Duck, goose, self-basting turkeys, or those with added fat; breaded and fried frozen meats, fish
Tuna canned in water or brine, canned salmon	Tuna in oil, luncheon meats, sausage, salami, rich pâté
Fruits and Vegetables	
Fresh fruits and vegetables	Avocados
Frozen fruits and vegetables	Canned vegetables (with salt or high-sodium compounds)
Canned vegetables including pulses (e.g sweetcorn, tomatoes, peas, baked beans, red kidney beans, chickpeas)	
Unsweetened juices	Sweetened juices
Tomato purée	
Fruits canned with natural juice	Canned fruits in heavy syrup
Breads and Cereals	
100% wholemeal bread	White bread, fancy breads
Whole wheat flour	
Prepared cereals without sugar, with 2 g or more fibre/serving	Sugar-coated cereals, with less than 2 g fibre/serving
Wholemeal buns, pitta bread, pasta and brown rice	
Fats, Seasonings, Desserts, Snacks	
Poly or mono-unsaturated margarines (p.208)	Butter, lard, hard margarines
Oils: sunflower, safflower, rapeseed, olive (p. 209)	Palm or coconut oils, partially hydrogenated vegetable oils
Low-fat or low-calorie mayonnaise	Mayonnaise
Low-fat or low-calorie salad dressings	Salad dressings unless low in fat or fat free
Fruit sorbets	Ice cream
Frozen juice bar, frozen yogurt bar	Ice cream bar
Plain biscuits, (e.g.) rich tea, ginger nut	Chocolates, many types of cakes, pies, peanuts, crisps
	Cream substitutes

A Guide to Food Labels

Don't be deceived by misleading food labels: the words "light" or "lite" may mean light in colour or light in calories, but not necessarily low in fat or calories. Read the list of ingredients and remember that ingredients are listed on the label in order of amounts by weight, beginning with the largest amount. Compare several different brands of the same product (per portion or per 100 g) and always choose the one that is lowest in fat.

*When you see "low fat" on the label, the food has less than *half* of the fat you would get in the normal product. However, bear in mind that it could still be quite high in fat compared with other foods.

*"Lower or reduced fat" means the food has not more than $\frac{3}{4}$ the fat of the normal product.

*The word "fat" may not appear on the label, but the following words all indicate fat: glycerides, glycerol, esters, shortening, hydrogenated oils.

*Foods containing large amounts of sugar should also be used sparingly. The word "sugar" may not appear, but the following words all mean sugar: fructose, sucrose, lactose, maltose, sorbitol, mannitol, dextrose, honey, syrups, molasses, sweeteners. Although foods may be labelled "no sugar added" or "unsweetened", they may still have a high content of natural sugar.

*Check the list of ingredients on bread packages to be sure that whole wheat or wholemeal is the first ingredient listed. Labels such as "bread with whole grain" or "whole-wheat goodness" may not mean whole wheat.

*"No cholesterol" is a meaningless claim often used on margarines or shortenings: foods from vegetable sources (i.e., vegetable oils) never contain cholesterol. However, they could have a high level of saturated fat, which raises the level of cholesterol in the blood.

---

*Foods advertised on a healthy theme might not be healthy and often may be high in sugar and fat; for example, the words pure, natural and wholesome have no nutritional meaning and are often perceived as implying that the product is healthy.

Previous page:
Rhubarb and Strawberry Sorbet (page 164), Pineapple and Orange Sorbet (page 165), Blackcurrant Sorbet (page 164)

Left:
Winter Fruit Compôte with Figs and Apricots (page 170)

Packed Lunches

Packed lunches allow you to control what you eat, save money and have good-tasting foods. With all the new vacuum-packed containers and insulated lunch bags the choice is unlimited. Some of the salads in this book, such as Pasta and Fresh Vegetable Salad (page 59) or White Bean, Radish and Red Onion Salad (page 47) are easy to pack and keep well. Also consider packing any of the soups from this book, either hot or cold.

When making sandwiches use a minimum of unsaturated margarine (avoid butter because it is high in saturated fat) or low-calorie mayonnaise, not both. To keep sandwiches moist I add sliced cucumber or tomato. To prevent the bread from going soggy I pack sliced tomatoes separately and add them to the sandwich just before eating.

I used to pack lunches for my children but after I got a few complaints and didn't remember who liked what, they decided to pack their own. I do try to make sure there is a good supply of the kinds of nutritious food they like. I keep wholemeal buns and crusty rolls in the freezer; carrots, celery, lettuce, cucumber, alfalfa sprouts, cheese and sliced turkey in the refrigerator; canned tuna and salmon, peanut butter and jam on the shelf, plus a good selection of fresh fruit.

My children don't often take raisins or dried fruit because they are too sweet, but my son often likes popcorn for a treat.

Tips When Using Pre-prepared Chilled or Frozen Meals

*Choose grilled, baked and stir-fry dishes; avoid ones with butter and cream sauces. Read the label and select ones with the lowest amount of fat and salt.

*Pre-prepared foods are usually low in fibre. Add fibre by eating wholemeal bread, split pea, lentil or vegetable soup, and a raw or cooked vegetable, and finish off with fruit.

*Portion sizes tend to be quite small. If you need more, fill up with crusts of chunky bread, pitta or extra rice, pasta or potatoes.

The Morning Meal

Some people are conditioned to eat breakfast while others aren't. The most important reasons for eating a good breakfast are:
*Studies have shown that children who have breakfast perform better at school than children who haven't.
*If you don't have breakfast it is more difficult to get all the nutrients you need in a day.
*People who maintain an ideal weight eat breakfast; overweight people tend to skip breakfast. If you miss breakfast and have a plain currant bun or wholemeal scone and an orange at coffee break, you are eating nutritiously; if you have a danish pastry and creamy coffee you are adding extra fat and calories without vitamins or fibre.

This doesn't mean you should be wolfing down fried eggs and bacon (too high in fat) but you should have some fruits or vegetables, milk, yogurt or low-fat cheese, and whole-grain toast or cereals. There's no need to limit your scope of breakfast foods. Dinner leftovers, a piece of pizza, fish or salad can be as good in the morning as at night.

Breakfast Cereals. It's important to read the labels, as some are much more nutritious than others. Read the ingredients per serving and the list of ingredients. Look for a short list of ingredients and one that begins with a whole grain, bran or oats. I let my children pick whatever cereals they like as long as they aren't high in sugar and have at least two grams of fibre per serving.

Many commercial mueslis are high in sugar and saturated fat from coconut oil. An alternative is to add dried fruits, such as raisins, chopped dates or apricots, and nuts to bran flakes or other low-sugar cereal. If you are on a salt-restricted diet, read the labels for salt, as many cereals are high in these.

Fruit, fruit juices or fruit drinks. Choose fruit juices rather than other drinks; fruit drinks or squash are fortified with vitamin C, but contain added sugar and don't have other nutrients that juices have. Choose fruit instead of juice for more fibre. Children don't need more than two drinks of juice a day; after that they are mainly getting sugar and might as well be drinking soft drinks. Instead, make sure they are drinking enough milk; after that give them water.

Eggs. Egg yolks are quite high in cholesterol but eggs are not high in total fat. So, providing you are eating a diet which is low in total fat, 4–6 eggs per week in the total diet is fine. For young children and the elderly, eggs are an easily digested and excellent source of protein and other nutrients, especially iron, so should not be restricted to less than six. Due to the salmonella risk of raw and lightly cooked eggs, they should always be cooked until both yolk and white are no longer runny for vulnerable groups like very young children, pregnant women and the elderly.

Bacon. Bacon is high in saturated fat, salt and nitrates and should be avoided or eaten only occasionally.

Cereal/Muesli Squares

Cereal/Muesli bars tend to be fairly high in both added sugar and fat — sometimes being the same as a chocolate bar! Check the label of shop-bought and always go for the one with the lowest fat and sugar content. Alternatively, try these tasty, easy-to-make squares that have a minimum of saturated fat and a maximum of fibre. They're great for school lunches.

PER SQUARE	
calories	104
g fat	5
g protein	2
g carbohydrate	15
Good: fibre	

$2\frac{1}{2}$ oz	unsaturated margarine	65 g
6 fl oz	liquid honey	180 ml
2 oz	brown sugar	50 g
8 oz	rolled oats	200 g
$4\frac{1}{2}$ oz	wholemeal flour	130 g
$4\frac{1}{2}$ oz	sunflower seeds	130 g
6 oz	chopped dried apricots, dates or raisins, or a combination	160 g
2 oz	chopped nuts (walnuts, pecans)	50 g
1 oz	sesame seeds	25 g

In small saucepan, melt margarine over low heat. Add honey and sugar; stir and bring to boil. Simmer for 5 minutes; remove from heat and let cool slightly.

In large bowl, combine rolled oats, flour, sunflower seeds, dried fruit, nuts and sesame seeds. Gradually stir in sugar mixture. Firmly press into lightly greased 11 × 7 in (2 lit) baking dish; bake in 350°F (180°C) Gas Mark 4 oven for 15 minutes or until golden. Let cool and cut into squares. Makes about 40.

Snacks

Snacks are part of our lifestyle and an important part of most children's daily food intake. Healthy snacking doesn't mean never having crisps or soft drinks, but rather saving them for special occasions and more often having fruit, yogurt, a currant bun, certain cereals, or a glass of milk. It's not fair never to let children taste the latest popular snack foods, but they don't need to have them every day. If you keep raw carrots, celery, cauliflower and green peppers ready in the refrigerator, I think you'll be surprised at how often children will choose them. To prevent loss of vitamins, keep raw vegetables in a plastic bag, not in water.

Pitta Pizzas are a healthy snack that the whole family will enjoy. The topping is low-calorie; see the comparison after the recipe for how it compares against a more conventional topping.

PER 2-PITA SERVING	
calories	286
g fat	6
g protein	23
g carbohydrate	41
Good: vitamin A, thiamin, riboflavin, calcium, fibre, iron	
Excellent: vitamin C, niacin	

Pitta Pizzas

A quick snack, lunch or light supper is easy to make using pitta bread rounds as a base. Instead of mushrooms, you can add a topping of a combination of red, yellow or green peppers, slice onion, sliced tomatoes, sliced artichokes, chopped fresh basil and broccoli. Instead of pittas you can substitute bread rolls, split in half, buns, tortillas, tostadas or courgettes halved lengthwise.

4	wholemeal pittas (6 to 8 in [15 to 20 cm] rounds)	
¾ lb	fresh mushrooms, thickly sliced	30C
4 fl oz	water	125 r
¾ lb	low-fat cottage cheese	30C
2 oz	grated low-fat mozzarella or cheddar	5C
1 tsp	dried thyme	5 r
1 tsp	dried oregano	5 r
3 oz	tomato purée	75
4 fl oz	water	125 r
1 tsp	granulated sugar	5 r
½ oz	chopped fresh chives or parsley	15

Cut around edge of each pitta to separate into 2 rounds; plac on baking sheet. Grill for 1 to 2 minutes on each side or until crisp.

In pan, simmer mushrooms with water over medium heat, covered, for 5 minutes or until tender; drain and set aside.

In bowl or food processor, combine cottage cheese, mozzarella, thyme and oregano; set aside.

Combine tomato purée, water and sugar; mix well. Spread tomato mixture over pittas; top with cheese mixture. Spoon mushrooms over pittas and bake in 400°F (200°C) Gas Mark 6 oven for 10 to 15 minutes or until heated through. Sprinkle wit chives or parsley. Makes 4 servings of 2 pizzas each.

omparisons of Snack Foods	g fat	calories
ixed nuts dry roasted, unsalted (1 oz [25 g])	17	197
ixed nuts, oil roasted plus salt (1 oz [25 g])	19	210
otato chips (10)	7	105
etzels, bread stick (5)	trace	59
oughnut, yeast type	11	174
hocolate-chip cookies (2)	6	103
ilk-chocolate bar (30 g)	10	156
e cream, 10% B.F. (5 oz [125 g])	8	142
uit yogurt, (1 pot [150 g])	2	140
uit lollipop	0	50
ople	0	84
anana	0	105
Club Biscuit (22 g)	6	114
igestive biscuits (2)	5	118
ch Tea biscuits (2)	2	59
g rolls (2)	2	24
urrant bun (60 g) } no butter	5	181
holemeal scone (60 g) } or margarine	9	196

Appendices

The Food Guide

Follow this healthy eating guide to obtain all the nutrients your body needs. For additional energy, increase the number and size of servings from the various food groups and/or add other foods.

Choose different kinds of foods from within each group to maintain your ideal weight. Select and prepare foods with limited amounts of fat, sugar and salt.

Milk and Milk Products

Children up to 11 years	2–3 servings
Adolescents	3–4 servings
Pregnant and nursing women	3–4 servings
Adults	2 servings

Some examples of one serving:
½ pt (300 ml) milk
6 oz (150 g) yogurt
1½ oz (40 g) Cheddar cheese

Breads and Cereals
3 to 5 servings, whole-grain products recommended

Some examples of one serving:
1 slice wholemeal bread
1½ oz (40 g) cooked cereal
1½ oz (40 g) ready-to-eat cereal
1 bread roll or 1 tbsp cooked rice, macaroni, spaghetti

Fruits and Vegetables
4–5 servings, choose a variety of fruits and vegetables (including at least 2 vegetables), cooked, raw or in their juices; include yellow and green vegetables

Some examples of one serving:
4 oz (100 g) fruits or vegetables or juice
1 medium-size potato, carrot, tomato, peach, orange or banana

Meat, Fish, Poultry and Alternatives
2 servings
Some examples of one serving:
2 to 3 oz (50 to 75 g) cooked lean meat, fish, poultry or liver
5 oz (125 g) peanut butter*
7 oz (175 g) cooked dried peas, beans, or lentils
2 oz (50 g) cheese*
3 oz (75 g) cottage cheese
2 eggs*
2 oz (50 g) nuts or seeds*

---

*These should be used less often because of their higher fat.

Foods High in Fibre

As a general guide, choose one or two servings from the list of foods highest in fibre and six to eight servings from the good sources of fibre. It's important to have at least eight glasses (8 fl oz [250 ml] each) of liquid a day.

Foods Highest in Fibre (over 4 g fibre/serving)
Cereals (1½ oz [40 g]): bran-type cereals, cereal with more than 4 g of fibre per serving
Legumes (4 oz [100 g], cooked): baked beans, kidney beans, butter beans, split peas, lentils
Fruits (6 pieces): dried dates, figs, prunes, raisins (1½ oz [40 g])
Nuts (2 oz [50 g]): peanuts, almonds, Brazil nuts

Good Fibre Sources (over 2 g fibre/serving)
Breads and Cereals: cereals with 2 g or more fibre per serving, 2 slices wholewheat, rye or cracked wheat bread, multi-grain or high fibre white bread, wholemeal rolls, bulgur or cracked wheat

Fruits (1 whole or 4 oz [100 g]): apple, banana, blackberries, cantaloupe melons, dates, orange, papaya, pear, raspberries, strawberries, dried apricots (6)

Vegetables (3 oz [75 g] or 1 whole): beans (green or yellow), broccoli, Brussels sprouts, carrots, sweetcorn, peas, baked potato, parsnips, spinach, sweet potato, turnip

Buying Guide for Spreading Fats

This is only a partial list of recommended spreading fats. Hard margarines aren't recommended because they tend to be too high in saturated fats.

Check the label and choose margarines that have at least 40 percent unsaturated fatty acids and not more than 18 percent saturated fatty acids.

Spreading Fats

Product	Energy per 25 g/oz kcals	Energy per 25 g/oz kj	Total fat per 100 g	Main type of fat
Suet, lard, dripping	255	1070	100	Saturated
Ghee	255	1070	100	Saturated
Butter (all brands)	210	880	80	Saturated
Concentrated butter	250	1050	100	Saturated
Reduced fat butters (e.g., Half fat Anchor)	110	460	40	Saturated
Hard Margarine (e.g., Echo)	210	880	80	Monounsaturated
Soft margarine (e.g., Stork SB)	210	880	80	Monounsaturated
Polyunsaturated margarine (e.g., Flora, Vitalite, Supermarket own, Sunflower/Soya Margarine)	210	880	80	Polyunsaturated
Low fat spreads				
Anchor Low Fat Clover Light	110	460	40	Saturated
Gold Delight	110	460	40	Monounsaturated
Shape LF Sunflower Slimmers Gold Sunflower Flora Lite	110	460	40	Polyunsaturated
Gold Lowest	80	336	25	Polyunsaturated
Full fat spreads Clover Golden Churn	195	820	75	Saturated
Meadow Cup	185	777	75	Saturated
Willow	200	840	80	Saturated

Buying Guide for Vegetable Oils

Look for oils with a high percentage of monounsaturated or polyunsaturated fatty acids and a low amount of saturated fatty acids. Bear in mind that coconut and palm oil have a higher saturated fat content than some animal fats. Rapeseed, safflower and sunflower oils are the best all-round oils.

TYPE	FATTY ACID CONTENT			UNSATURATED/ SATURATED FAT RATIO	COMMENT
	POLY-UNSATURATED (%)	MONO-UNSATURATED (%)	SATURATED (%)		
Rapeseed	32	62	6	15.7:1	best fatty acid ratio
Safflower	75	12	9	9.6:1	highest in polyunsaturates
Sunflower	66	20	10	8.6:1	sometimes used in place of olive oil, but blander
Corn	59	24	13	6.4:1	heavy taste, often used for deep frying
Soyabean	59	23	14	5.9:1	most commonly used oil — in baked goods, salad dressings, margarine, mayonnaise
Olive	9	72	14	5.8:1	highest in monounsaturated fat; expensive
Peanut	32	46	17	4.6:1	more pronounced flavour than most oils
Sesame seed	40	40	18	4.4:1	used in Oriental and Middle Eastern cooking; flavourful
Cottonseed	52	18	26	2.7:1	comparatively high in saturated fat; used in processed foods and salad dressings
Palm	2	10	80	0.2:1	the only vegetable oils high in saturated fat. Used in baked goods and sweets; not recommended
Coconut	2	6	87	0.1:1	

Note: Other substances, such as water and vitamins, make up the total composition (100%).
Taken from an article in the *University of California, Berkeley Wellness Letter*, Volume 3, Issue 6, March 1987.

Buying Guide for Cheeses

LOW FAT (under 20g fat per 100g cheese)		MEDIUM FAT (21g to 30g fat per 100g cheese)		HIGH FAT (over 31g fat per 100g cheese)	
Quark	neg	French Camembert	20–23	Philadelphia	30
Cottage Cheese	2–7	Cheese spread	21	Emmental	30–35
Fromage Frais	4	St. Paulin	22	Blue and White Stilton	31–35
Italian Ricotta	4	St. Moret	22	Caerphilly	32
French Jockey	8	Austrian Smoked	23	Wensleydale	32
Shape	9	Goat	23–27	Gouda	32
Low fat cheese spread	9	Edam	24	Double Gloucester	32
Low fat Edam	11	Gorganzola	24	Gruyere	32
Curd Cheese	12	French Mini Babybel	24	Roquefort	32
Light Philadelphia	15	Somerset Brie	24	Cheddar	33–35
Tendale	15	Bel Paese	25	Roule	33
Parmesan	varies 17–25	Bresse Bleu	25	Vegetarian Cheddar	37–40
Danish Feta	18	Danish Samose	25	French Boursin	38
		Flora Cheese Spread	25	Cambazola	42
		Danish Havarti	26	Danish Brie	42
		Danish Blue	27–30	German Blue Brie	42
		Mozzarella	29	Cream Cheese	45

Recommended daily amounts of food energy and some nutrients for population groups in United Kingdom

Age range[a] years	Occupational category	Energy[b] MJ	Kcal	Protein[c] g	Thiamin mg	Riboflavin mg
Boys						
under 1					0.3	0.4
1		5.0	1200	30	0.5	0.6
2		5.75	1400	35	0.6	0.7
3–4		6.5	1560	39	0.6	0.8
5–6		7.25	1740	43	0.7	0.9
7–8		8.25	1980	49	0.8	1.0
9–11		9.5	2280	57	0.9	1.2
12–14		11.0	2640	66	1.1	1.4
15–17		12.0	2880	72	1.2	1.7
Girls						
under 1					0.3	0.4
1		4.5	1100	27	0.4	0.6
2		5.5	1300	32	0.5	0.7
3–4		6.25	1500	37	0.6	0.8
5–6		7.0	1680	42	0.7	0.9
7–8		8.0	1900	47	0.8	1.0
9–11		8.5	2050	51	0.8	1.2
12–14		9.0	2150	53	0.9	1.4
15–17		9.0	2150	53	0.9	1.7
Men						
18–34	Sedentary	10.5	2510	63	1.0	1.6
	Moderately active	12.0	2900	72	1.2	1.6
	Very active	14.0	3350	84	1.3	1.6
35–64	Sedentary	10.0	2400	60	1.0	1.6
	Moderately active	11.5	2750	69	1.1	1.6
	Very active	14.0	3350	84	1.3	1.6
65–74	Assuming a	10.0	2400	60	1.0	1.6
75+	sedentary life	9.0	2150	54	0.9	1.6
Women						
18–54	Most occupations	9.0	2150	54	0.9	1.3
	Very active	10.5	2500	62	1.0	1.3
55–74	Assuming a	8.0	1900	47	0.8	1.3
75+	sedentary life	7.0	1680	42	0.7	1.3
Pregnancy		10.0	2400	60	1.0	1.6
Lactation		11.5	2750	69	1.1	1.8

Notes
(a) Since these recommendations (published in 1979) are average amounts, the figures for each age range represent the amounts recommended at the middle of the range. Within each age range, younger children will need less, and older children more, than the amount recommended.
(b) Megajoules (10^6 joules). Calculated from the relation 1 kilocalorie = 4.184 kilojoules, that is to say, 1 megajoule = 240 kilocalories.
(c) Recommended amounts have been calculated as 10% of the recommendations for energy (paragraph 44).
(d) 1 nicotinic acid equivalent = 1 mg available nicotinic acid or 60 mg tryptophan.

Nicotinic acid equivalents mg[d]	Total folate[e] μg	Ascorbic acid mg	Vitamin A retinol equivalents μg[f]	Vitamin D[g] cholecalciferal μg	Calcium mg	Iron mg
5	50	20	450	7.5	600	6
7	100	20	300	10	600	7
8	100	20	300	10	600	7
9	100	20	300	10	600	8
10	200	20	300	[g]	600	10
11	200	20	400	[g]	600	10
14	200	25	575	[g]	700	12
16	300	25	725	[g]	700	12
19	300	30	750	[g]	600	12
5	50	20	450	7.5	600	6
7	100	20	300	10	600	7
8	100	20	300	10	600	7
9	100	20	300	10	600	8
10	200	20	300	[g]	600	10
11	200	20	400	[g]	600	10
14	300	25	575	[g]	700	12[i]
16	300	25	725	[g]	700	12[i]
19	300	30	750	[g]	600	12[i]
18	300	30	750	[g]	500	10
18	300	30	750	[g]	500	10
18	300	30	750	[g]	500	10
18	300	30	750	[g]	500	10
18	300	30	750	[g]	500	10
18	300	30	750	[g]	500	10
18	300	30	750	[g]	500	10
18	300	30	750	[g]	500	10
15	300	30	750	[g]	500	12[i]
15	300	30	750		500	12[i]
15	300	30	750	[g]	500	10
15	300	30	750	[g]	500	10
18	500	60	750	10	1200[h]	13
21	400	60	1200	10	1200	15

(e) No information is available about requirements of children for folate. Graded amounts are recommended between the figure shown for infants under 1 year, which is based upon the average folate content of mature human milk and the 300 μg daily which is suggested for adults.

(f) 1 retinal equivalent = 1 μg retinol of 6 μgβ-carotene or 12 μg other biologically active carotenoids.

(g) No dietary sources may be necessary for children and adults who are sufficiently exposed to sunlight, but during the winter children and adolescents should receive 10 μg (400 i.u.) daily by supplementation. Adults with inadequate exposure to sunlight, for example who are housebound, may also need a supplement of 10 μg daily (para 60).

(h) For the third trimester only.

(i) This intake may not be sufficient for 10% of girls and women with large menstrual losses.

Height/Weight Chart

Men weight (Imperial) in indoor clothing and without shoes

Height	Acceptable Weight Range	Obese
5 ft 2 in	8 st 0 lb–10 st 1 lb	12 st 1 lb
5 ft 3 in	8 st 3 lb–10 st 4 lb	12 st 5 lb
5 ft 4 in	8 st 6 lb–10 st 8 lb	12 st 10 lb
5 ft 5 in	8 st 9 lb–10 st 12 lb	13 st 0 lb
5 ft 6 in	8 st 12 lb–11 st 2 lb	13 st 5 lb
5 ft 7 in	9 st 2 lb–11 st 7 lb	13 st 11 lb
5 ft 8 in	9 st 6 lb–11 st 12 lb	14 st 3 lb
5 ft 9 in	9 st 10 lb–12 st 2 lb	14 st 8 lb
5 ft 10 in	10 st 0 lb–12 st 6 lb	14 st 13 lb
5 ft 11 in	10 st 4 lb–12 st 11 lb	15 st 5 lb
6 ft 0 in	10 st 8 lb–13 st 2 lb	15 st 11 lb
6 ft 1 in	10 st 12 lb–13 st 7 lb	16 st 3 lb
6 ft 2 in	11 st 2 lb–13 st 12 lb	16 st 9 lb
6 ft 3 in	11 st 6 lb–14 st 3 lb	17 st 1 lb
6 ft 4 in	11 st 10 lb–14 st 8 lb	17 st 7 lb

Men weight without clothes (metric)
Add 3 kg if you weigh yourself in your clothes

Height	Acceptable Weight Range	Obese
1.60 m	52 kg–65 kg	78 kg
1.62 m	53 kg–65 kg	79 kg
1.64 m	54 kg–67 kg	80 kg
1.66 m	55 kg–69 kg	83 kg
1.68 m	56 kg–71 kg	85 kg
1.70 m	58 kg–73 kg	88 kg
1.72 m	59 kg–74 kg	89 kg
1.74 m	60 kg–75 kg	90 kg
1.76 m	62 kg–77 kg	92 kg
1.78 m	64 kg–79 kg	95 kg
1.80 m	65 kg–80 kg	96 kg
1.82 m	66 kg–82 kg	98 kg
1.84 m	67 kg–84 kg	101 kg
1.86 m	69 kg–86 kg	103 kg
1.88 m	71 kg–88 kg	106 kg

Women weight (Imperial) in indoor clothing and without shoes

Height	Acceptable Weight Range	Obese
4 ft 10 in	6 st 13 lb– 8 st 10 lb	10 st 6 lb
4 ft 11 in	7 st 1 lb– 8 st 12 lb	10 st 10 lb
5 ft 0 in	7 st 3 lb– 9 st 1 lb	10 st 13 lb
5 ft 1 in	7 st 6 lb– 9 st 4 lb	11 st 2 lb
5 ft 2 in	7 st 10 lb– 9 st 8 lb	11 st 7 lb
5 ft 3 in	7 st 12 lb– 9 st 10 lb	11 st 11 lb
5 ft 4 in	8 st 0 lb–10 st 1 lb	12 st 1 lb
5 ft 5 in	8 st 5 lb–10 st 6 lb	12 st 6 lb
5 ft 6 in	8 st 7 lb–10 st 8 lb	12 st 10 lb
5 ft 7 in	8 st 9 lb–10 st 12 lb	13 st 1 lb
5 ft 8 in	9 st 0 lb–11 st 2 lb	13 st 5 lb
5 ft 9 in	9 st 2 lb–11 st 5 lb	13 st 9 lb
5 ft 10 in	9 st 4 lb–11 st 9 lb	14 st 0 lb
5 ft 11 in	9 st 8 lb–12 st 0 lb	14 st 4 lb
6 ft 0 in	9 st 11 lb–12 st 2 lb	14 st 6 lb

Women weight without clothes (metric)
Add 2 kg if you weigh yourself in your clothes

Height	Acceptable Weight Range	Obese
1.48 m	44 kg–55 kg	66 kg
1.50 m	45 kg–56 kg	68 kg
1.52 m	46 kg–58 kg	69 kg
1.54 m	47 kg–59 kg	71 kg
1.56 m	49 kg–61 kg	73 kg
1.58 m	50 kg–62 kg	75 kg
1.60 m	51 kg–64 kg	77 kg
1.62 m	53 kg–66 kg	79 kg
1.64 m	54 kg–67 kg	81 kg
1.66 m	55 kg–69 kg	83 kg
1.68 m	57 kg–71 kg	85 kg
1.70 m	58 kg–72 kg	87 kg
1.72 m	59 kg–74 kg	89 kg
1.74 m	61 kg–76 kg	91 kg
1.76 m	62 kg–77 kg	93 kg

With thanks to the Scottish Health Education Group

INDEX

OTHER GRUB STREET COOKERY BOOKS

The Essential Olive Oil Companion
Anne Dolamore. Price £10.95. Cased.

Caribbean and African Cookery
Rosamund Grant
Foreword by Maya Angelou. Price £10.95. Cased.

Gourmet Barbecue
Charmaine Solomon. Price £6.95. Softback.

Carol Bowen's Microwave Cooking for One and Two
Carol Bowen. Price £7.95. Softback.

Basic Basics Combination & Microwave Handbook
Carol Bowen. Price £4.95. Softback.

Combination Oven Cookery
Caroline Stevens and Deborah Robb. Price £6.95. Softback.

NOTES